A Field Guide to the
GRASSHOPPERS AND CRICKETS
of Britain and Northern Europe

Translator's note

I should like to thank my husband David, who works on this group of insects at the Natural History Museum in London, for helping me with the technical entomological terms in this book. He has also provided the brief notes on the continental European and British distribution of each species, and adapted the German text for more general use in various other ways.

Binky Ragge

A Field Guide to the

GRASSHOPPERS AND CRICKETS

of Britain and Northern Europe

HEIKO BELLMANN

Translated by
BINKY RAGGE

COLLINS
8 Grafton Street, London

The cover pictures show: *Omocestus rufipes* (Woodland Grasshopper) ♂ (p. 172); *Meconema thalassinum* (Oak Bush-cricket) ♀ (p. 86, above).

Photograph on page 79 (above) R. Höfels, page 99 Dr S. Ingrisch, all other photographs and all drawings by the author.

ISBN 0-00-219852-5

Filmset by Ace Filmsetting Ltd, Frome, Somerset
Printed and bound by Druckerei Parzeller, Fulda, West Germany

CONTENTS

FOREWORD

Grasshoppers and crickets are among the most conspicuous insects, yet few people take a special interest in them. They offer many opportunities for observation, and the study of their highly-developed songs is one of the most fascinating fields of behavioural science. Many species, moreover, are indicators of undisturbed environmental conditions, and thus help to provide valuable evidence in recognizing habitats that are in need of protection. The reasons for the lack of interest in these insects lie partly in their often deep-rooted misconception as pests, and partly in the difficulties of identification. Until now there has been no readily understandable, well-illustrated identification manual for the northern European fauna. This deficiency should be remedied by the present book, in which all the native northern European grasshoppers and crickets, and usually both sexes, are illustrated in colour. I hope that this book will at last succeed in bringing to these insects the attention they deserve.

It was not easy to find all the species, some of which are extremely rare. Numerous journeys, often to distant regions, were necessary, and many well-known orthopterists have helped me with this. My thanks are particularly due to Dr H. Fischer, Dr K. Harz, Dr S. Ingrisch and Dr A. Nadig. Without their support many of the discoveries portrayed here in the coloured illustrations would not have been possible.

Ulm, March 1985 Heiko Bellmann

Classification

Among the insects (an extraordinarily rich group comprising about three-quarters of all known animal species) grasshoppers and crickets belong to the group Hemimetabola, insects with incomplete metamorphosis. They develop from the egg through a variable number of nymphal stages to the adult insect. The pupal stage, typical of insect metamorphosis, is thus missing. The closest relatives of the grasshoppers and crickets (order Saltatoria) are the cockroaches (Blattodea), earwigs (Dermaptera) and praying mantises (Mantodea). All four orders are together called Orthoptera. Within the Saltatoria two suborders are recognized: the Ensifera or crickets and bush-crickets, and the Caelifera or grasshoppers and ground-hoppers. The members of the two suborders may easily be distinguished by the different lengths of their antennae. Only the Mole-cricket causes difficulties: although belonging to the Ensifera, it has short antennae; it also lacks a second important character, the long ovipositor of the female.

Body Structure

The body is divided into three parts (*Fig. 1*): head, thorax and abdomen. The head bears a pair of antennae (feelers), mouthparts and eyes.

The mouthparts are of the primitive, biting type (in other insects there are many modifications, often for sucking or piercing). They consist of a pair of stout, toothed mandibles to bite off pieces of food, a pair of maxillae to masticate the food, and an unpaired labium, which prevents the food falling out. In order to hold the food better (and also to taste it) the maxillae and labium are equipped with long, jointed palps. The mouth appendages are covered by the labrum, an unpaired attachment to the clypeus.

The paired compound eyes are composed of a multitude of tiny 'single eyes'. Each of these produces an 'image-point', so that the insect obtains the equivalent of a very coarse newspaper photograph of its surroundings. On the front of the head there are three further, point-like, simple eyes – the ocelli. Their function is still not fully understood, but they are used, among other things, for seeing in dim light.

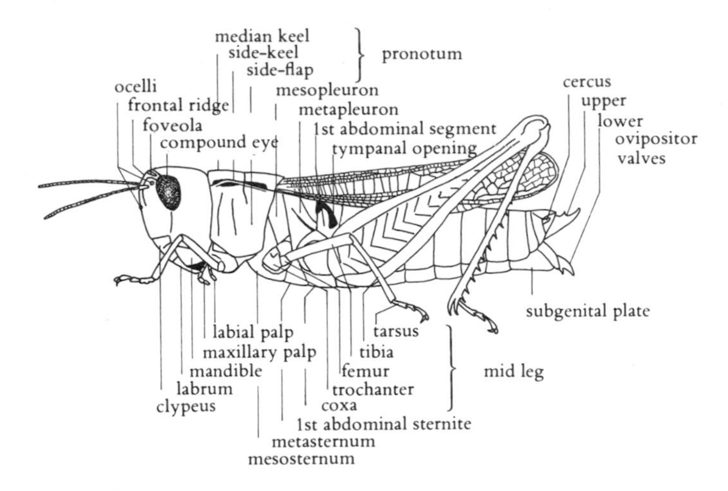

Fig. 1 Body structure of a grasshopper (*Stenobothrus lineatus* ♀); mouthparts only partly visible.

Two further characteristics of the head shown by grasshoppers are a broad frontal ridge (running vertically between the antennae) and the foveolae. The latter are triangular, trapezoid or rectangular depressions next to the compound eyes, not shown by all species but often important in classification.

The thorax consists of three segments, covered above by the pro-, meso- and metanotum. The sides of the two posterior segments (meso- and metapleuron) are each divided by a groove into an anterior and a posterior part. The corresponding parts of the ventral skeleton are called the pro-, meso- and metasternum. The pronotum is conspicuously enlarged in comparison with the other two thoracic segments. It often bears three longitudinal keels along the top: a median keel and two side-keels (the shape of which is often important in identification). About halfway along the pronotum there is a transverse groove dividing it into an anterior part, the prozona, and a posterior part, the metazona. The pronotal side-flaps reach downwards about as far as the base of the fore leg.

The thorax bears all the organs of locomotion: three pairs of legs and two pairs of wings. The legs are segmented into (from the body outwards) the coxa, trochanter, femur, tibia and tarsus, the last-mentioned with three or four tarsal segments and two claws at the tip. The hind legs are extraordi-

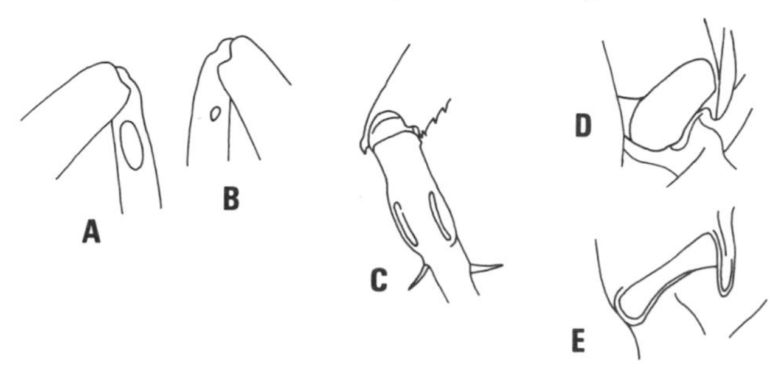

Fig. 2 Hearing organs: **A** *Gryllus campestris* ♂, outer side of the fore knee, **B** inner side of the same; **C** *Tettigonia viridissima* ♂, fore knee from the front; **D** *Chorthippus apricarius* ♀, right tympanal opening; **E** *Chorthippus biguttulus* ♀, right tympanal opening.

narily strongly developed: the femur contains the powerful jumping muscles, which give the Saltatoria their remarkable leaping ability. In the crickets and bush-crickets the hearing organs lie in the fore legs, just beyond the knee-joint (*Fig. 2* **A–C**). There are two tympanal membranes in each tibia, which communicate with the outside air through broadly oval (2 **A**) or slit-like (2 **C**) openings. In the crickets the inner tympana are often smaller (2 **B**) or completely absent.

The two pairs of wings are quite different from each other. The fore wings are narrow and more strongly sclerotized (hardened) than the hind wings. During flight the hind wings

Overleaf: *p. 10*, *Polysarcus denticauda* ♂, (Schlatt SA), July
p. 11, above left, *Ephippiger ephippiger* ♂, (Schlossböckelheim Pf), August
above right, *Stethophyma grossum* ♀, Fetzachmoos OS, September
below left, *Omocestus rufipes* ♂, Lautern SA, September
below right, *Gomphocerus sibiricus* ♂, Hochgurgl Ty, July

are spread like fans; when flexed they lie narrowly folded under the oblong fore wings. A study of the venation of the fore wings is frequently necessary in order to distinguish very similar grasshoppers from one another. The most important terms are therefore explained here (see *Fig. 3*). The longitudinal veins – from the fore margin to the hind margin (in the flexed wings from below to above) – are called the costa,

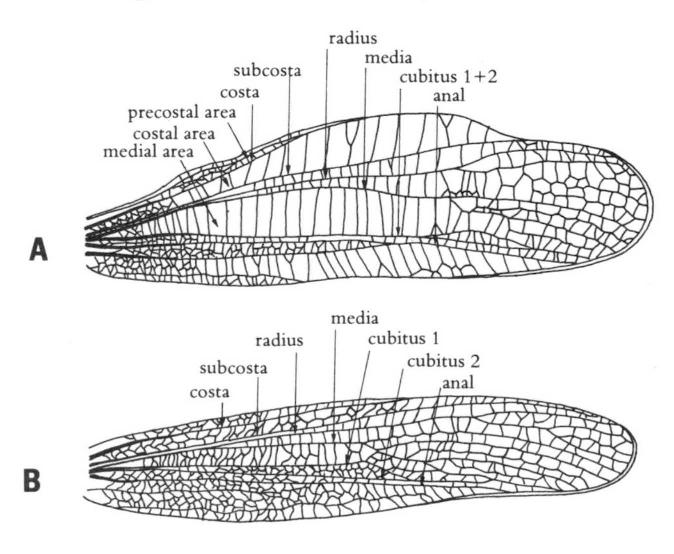

Fig. 3 Wing-venation of right fore wings: **A** *Stauroderus scalaris* ♂, **B** *Omocestus viridulus* ♀.

subcosta, radius, media, cubitus and anal veins. The cubitus is usually divided at the base into two veins. The areas between the veins are named after the veins forming their anterior border, so that the costal area lies behind the costa and the medial area behind the media. These two areas are often broadened (3 **A**). When the medial area is broadened the two cubital veins are usually fused together. Another wing area that is important in identification is the precostal area. This lies in front of the costa along the anterior margin of the fore wing, and in many species is broadened near the base of the wing (3 **A**). The hind wings are usually of minor importance in identifying the species; they can, however, be varyingly darkened or even uniformly brownish-black (*Arcyptera fusca*, *Stauroderus scalaris*). Six northern European species have brightly-coloured hind wings; their colouring and pattern make these species easy to recognize.

By no means all Saltatoria are capable of flight. The wings may be reduced to a varying extent; sometimes they are completely absent (*Tachycines asynamorus*, *Myrmecophilus acervorum*). Short-winged species can be confused with nymphs (the difference is explained in the section on nymphal development). In many species that are normally short-winged, fully-winged individuals occur occasionally (*p. 38*).

The third part of the body is formed by the abdomen, most of which is occupied by the digestive tract and the reproductive organs. It is covered on the outside by the tergites (along the back and sides) and sternites (below). In the grasshoppers the hearing organs lie on each side of the first abdominal segment (*Fig. 2* **D**, **E**). A narrow kidney-shaped, semicircular or oval opening leads to an obliquely sloping tympanal membrane. The tympanal opening is often difficult to find; the wings often partly cover it and one usually needs a lens.

The tip of the abdomen provides the most reliable way of distinguishing between the sexes (*Fig. 4*). All female Saltatoria (except the Mole-cricket) have a four-valved (two-valved in side view) ovipositor. In the Ensifera the upper and lower valves are tightly interlocked; in the Caelifera they can be spread apart like a pair of tongs. While the ovipositors of the crickets and bush-crickets are clearly visible as sickle-, sword- or rod-shaped appendages, the short ovipositor valves of the grasshoppers can be partly withdrawn into the

Overleaf: Mating
p. 14, above, *Isophya pyrenea,* (Schlatt SA), June
below, *Barbitistes serricauda*, ♀ eating the spermatophore, (Ulm SA), August

p. 15, above, *Myrmeleotettix maculatus*, Gosheim NöR, August
below, *Tetrix tuerki*, Reichenau Gr, August

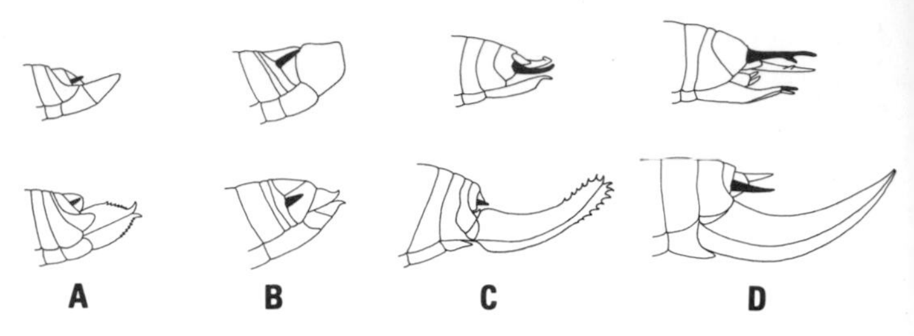

Fig. 4 Abdominal tips of male (upper row) and female (lower row) Orthoptera: **A** *Tetrix tenuicornis*, **B** *Chorthippus biguttulus*, **C** *Isophya pyrenea*, **D** *Metrioptera roeselii*; left cercus and style black.

abdomen. If one gently squeezes the abdomen of a living grasshopper, the valves protrude quite clearly.

In male grasshoppers and ground-hoppers the tip of the abdomen is rounded or pointed, depending on the shape of the subgenital plate. In its position of rest the subgenital plate (last abdominal sternite), which is hollowed out like a scoop, encloses the male genitalia. In male Ensifera the subgenital plate is flat or slightly curved, often bilobed at the tip and equipped with paired appendages – the styles (absent in the northern European Phaneropterinae). The male cerci of the Ensifera are very conspicuous and characteristic of the species (*Fig. 5*). They can be curved or toothed in distinctive ways and are often a reliable diagnostic character.

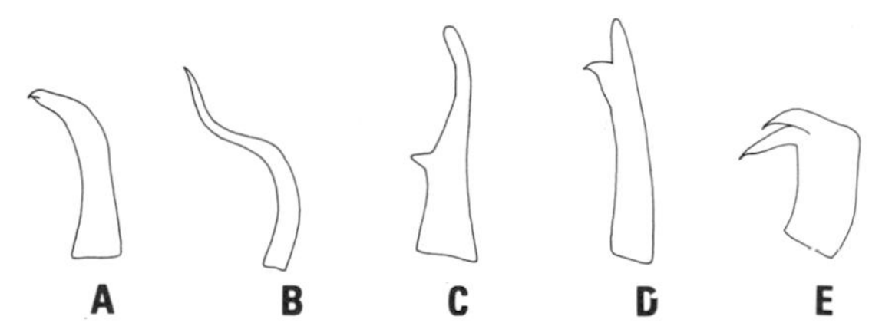

Fig. 5 Left cerci of male bush-crickets: **A** *Polysarcus denticauda*, **B** *Barbitistes serricauda*, **C** *Tettigonia cantans*, **D** *Metrioptera bicolor*, **E** *Ruspolia nitidula*.

Ecology

The various species of Saltatoria demand very different requirements from their environment. Some species, such as *Tettigonia viridissima* and *Chorthippus parallelus*, thrive in a wide variety of living conditions and consequently occur in widely differing habitats; these are known as euryoecious species. Others, the so-called stenoecious species, can live only in very specific places that exactly satisfy their demands. Examples of these are the inhabitants of the gravel-banks of alpine streams, e.g., *Tetrix tuerki* and *Bryodema tuberculata*. Such species are particularly vulnerable to environmental changes (see the section on conservation).

Since most of the northern European Saltatoria originated in warmer zones, such as the Mediterranean region, the temperature is the main limiting factor for many of them. Some can maintain themselves in the long term only in man-made buildings (*Tachycines asynamorus*, *Acheta domesticus*); others are confined to the warmest and driest regions (e.g., *Ephippiger ephippiger*, *Calliptamus italicus*). In addition to the warmth-loving species there are also cold-tolerant ones, which occur only in mountains (*Gomphocerus sibiricus*). There are also species that prefer damp places, for example the *Conocephalus* species and *Stethophyma grossum*.

One can often quite easily establish from the different Saltatoria occurring within an apparently uniform area, that there is in fact a mosaic of small patches providing quite different living conditions. *Myrmeleotettix maculatus* and *Omocestus rufipes*, for example, can occur abundantly in the dry parts of a moorland area; in depressions that are only slightly damp, they are replaced by *Chorthippus dorsatus* and *Metrioptera brachyptera*; and in marshy hollows, their places are taken by *Stethophyma grossum* and *Chorthippus montanus*. The euryoecious species, like *Chorthippus parallelus* and

Overleaf: Egg-laying
p. 18, above, Isophya pyrenea, (Schlatt SA), June
below, *Conocephalus discolor*, (Riedheim BS), September

p. 19, above, Chrysochraon dispar, (Weissingen BS), September
below, *Oedipoda caerulescens*, (Jockgrim Pf), September

Chrysochraon brachyptera, can occur over the whole area. Thus, as with plant communities, associations of Saltatoria are each characteristic of well-defined environmental conditions (Ingrisch 1982). The stenoecious species are excellent indicators of unchanged environmental conditions when they live year after year in exactly the same places, and of a change in these conditions when they disappear.

Dry fields with short grass provide especially rich habitats for Saltatoria, as do damp meadows and sunny woodland borders. One naturally finds the greatest variety of species in regions that offer very varied living conditions in a small area. Moors that are dry round the perimeter and wet in the centre satisfy these requirements particularly well. In one moorland area of about 2 km diameter, I was able to detect twenty-three different species within a few days. A few visits are often sufficient for a survey of this kind, as in high and late summer (end of July to end of September) one can find almost all the species at the same time.

Feeding Habits

The view generally prevails that the Saltatoria are herbivorous and therefore harmful. This belief stems from the locust swarms of times long past. Only the grasshoppers, groundhoppers and phaneropterine bush-crickets are pure herbivores. Even then most of the Caelifera eat just grasses; they feed on other plants only exceptionally. Almost all Tettigoniidae have a mixed diet. They eat small, soft-skinned insects, like caterpillars and greenflies, as well as various plants, especially those of a succulent kind (e.g., dandelion, chickweed and clover species). The proportions of animal and plant constituents in the diet vary from species to species. The large bush-crickets, like the Great Green Bush-cricket and the Wart-biter, appear to feed predominantly on other insects; they even eat the larvae of the Colorado Beetle, which are rejected by most predators. The oak bush-crickets live exclusively on other insects, particularly greenflies. Even the much-abused Mole-cricket apparently prefers to eat insect larvae, e.g., those of cockchafers and owlet moths. The alleged damage caused by Saltatoria is greatly exaggerated; many species prove, on the contrary, to be very beneficial.

Song

The Saltatoria produce a greater variety of differentiated sounds than any other insect order. The sounds are produced mainly by the males, using various quite different structures.

In nearly all Ensifera both fore wings are slightly raised and then rubbed against each other (*p. 117*) In the crickets the right fore wing generally lies on top, in the bush-crickets the left one; the Mole-cricket sometimes has one fore wing on top and sometimes the other. The sound is produced by a stridulatory ridge with cross-ribs (*Fig. 6* **B**) – on the underside of the upper fore wing – being rubbed over a scraper on the lower fore wing (*Fig. 6* **A**: Sc). In the crickets the sound-producing structures are similarly developed in both fore

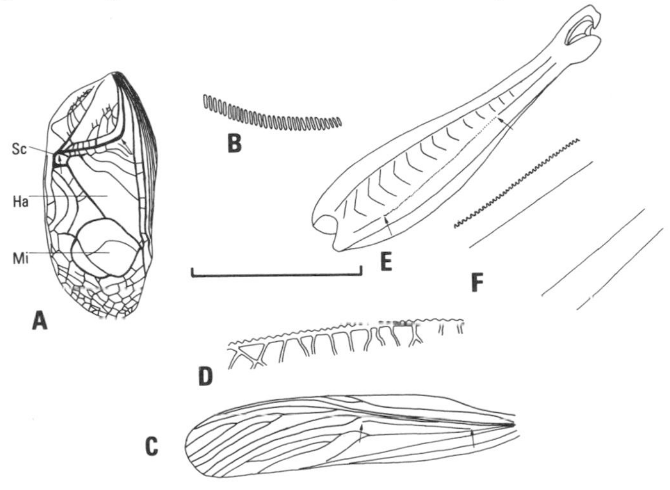

Fig. 6 Stridulatory organs: **A** *Gryllus campestris* ♂, right fore wing (Ha: harp, Mi: mirror, Sc: scraper), **B** the same, part of the stridulatory ridge; **C** *Psophus stridulus* ♂, left fore wing, **D** the same, part of the stridulatory ridge (viewed from the posterior margin of the wing); **E** *Gomphocerus sibiricus* ♂, inner side of right hind femur, **F** the same, part of the stridulatory ridge (viewed from below, the lines showing the longitudinal keel and the outer side of the femur). The scale line denotes 1mm for **B**, **D**, **F**. The stridulatory ridge lies between the arrows in **A**, **C**, **E**.

wings. The sound is amplified by two large membranous surfaces, the harp and mirror (*Fig. 6* **A**: Ha, Mi) (in the bush-crickets only by the mirror). The grasshoppers rub one or both hind femora over the fore wings. In the gomphocerine grasshoppers, a toothed ridge on the inner side of the hind femur (*Fig. 6* **E**, **F**) is rubbed over the projecting radius of the fore wing. The 'sounding-board' is formed by the roof-shaped arrangement of the fore wings, which enclose an interspace between them and the abdomen.

In the locustine grasshoppers, the ridge on the inner side of the hind femora is untoothed; they have instead a special intercalary vein (missing in the Gomphocerinae) in the medial area of the fore wings (*Fig. 6* **C**). This vein is clearly raised up from the wing surface; it bears little rounded teeth along its entire length (*Fig. 6* **D**).

Stethophyma grossum, the Large Marsh Grasshopper, has developed a different method of singing from the other Locustinae. It lifts one hind femur and flicks the tibia backwards. In this way it scrapes the apical spurs of the hind tibiae over the intercalary vein and produces the characteristic tibial 'flick-sound', reminiscent of snapping one's fingernails.

The spine-breasted grasshoppers stridulate by rubbing together the chewing surfaces of their mandibles, comparable to 'teeth-gnashing'. The soft rustling sounds are perceptible only from a short distance.

The sound-production of *Meconema thalassinum*, the Oak Bush-cricket, is particularly unusual. It raises one of its hind legs and drums with the tarsus on the substrate, usually a leaf. The purring sound produced is audible from about 1m.

Some grasshoppers (*Psophus stridulus*, *Bryodema tuberculata*, *Arcyptera fusca* and *Stauroderus scalaris*) produce a clear whirring sound in flight, even a conspicuous rattle in the case of *Psophus*. The origin of this sound does not yet seem to be fully understood. In these species every other longitudinal vein of the hind wing is noticeably strengthened (clearly visible on *p. 149*, above). The sound could be produced by an up–down vibration of the pairs of wing-areas lying between these stronger veins (and in turn linked together by a weaker longitudinal vein).

In many Saltatoria, especially the grasshoppers, the

females also sing. Female grasshoppers have a similar stridulatory file to that of the males but in a reduced form. The songs of the females generally indicate that they are ready for mating. They are significantly quieter than the male songs and rarely heard. They do not therefore play an important part in identification.

Most of the bush-crickets produce just one kind of song, which is influenced only by the temperature. *Tettigonia cantans*, for example, produces a continuous buzz in warm weather, but in the evening, when the temperature drops to 15°C or less, the individual syllables are clearly audible. Apart from the effect of temperature, different kinds of song are rarely found in bush-crickets. The greatly varied song of *Polysarcus denticauda* is an exception. It is composed of a series of buzzing sounds of different frequency, as well as quite sharp single syllables. In the Field-cricket (and also in the other crickets) there are different kinds of song: the calling song to attract the female and establish the territory, the fighting song of two males and the courtship song as a prelude to mating.

A similar variety of different kinds of song is characteristic of most grasshoppers. There is never fighting between males, but only rivalry singing, which is enough to keep the males apart. The courtship songs are variously graded according to the increasing proximity of the male and female, and their eventual mating.

Overleaf: *p. 24*, Eggs
above left, *Phaneroptera falcata*, (Jockgrim Pf), September
above right, *Chrysochraon dispar*, (Weissingen BS), September
below left, *Oedipoda caerulescens*, (Jockgrim Pf), September
below right, *Chrysochraon brachypterus*, Baustetten OS, August

p. 25, Nymphs
above left, *Barbitistes serricauda*, last nymphal instar ♀, (Ulm SA), July
above right, *Conocephalus discolor*, penultimate nymphal instar ♀, Riedheim BS, July
below left, *Chrysochraon brachypterus*, last nymphal instar ♀, Arnegg SA, June
below right, *Psophus stridulus*, last nymphal instar ♂, (Solnhofen FrA), July

Mating

The Ensifera and Caelifera differ fundamentally in the way in which mating takes place. In the grasshoppers and groundhoppers the female behaves mainly passively, although she can show her readiness (perhaps through a special song) or unreadiness (e.g., through defensive movements with the hind tibiae) for mating. The male mounts and couples with the female by moving the tip of his abdomen to one side of the female abdomen and then gripping the tip of her abdomen below. The male often allows himself to fall backwards and is then dragged along by the female, lying on his back (*p. 15*, above). In most species, mating lasts quite a long time (20 mins to several hours).

In the bush-crickets the female takes a more active part. Attracted by the male's song, she approaches him, provided she is in a receptive state for mating. Eventually she climbs on to the back of the male, who then grasps the tip of her abdomen with his cerci. In many species, a very large, whitish spermatophore then emerges from the male genital opening, and this is attached to the female genital opening. The spermatophore consists of a gelatinous substance, which encloses the sperm. It is often divided into several globular parts. Shortly after the emergence of the spermatophore the couple separate. In many species the mating process ends after a few (2–5) minutes, in others it lasts up to half an hour. Immediately after the couple separate, the female begins to eat the gelatinous substance. During the eating process, which usually lasts several hours, the sperm enter the female genital opening. In many Ensifera there are deviations from the mating position described above; e.g., the male may turn to face backwards or stand on his head.

Egg-laying

A few days after mating, the female begins egg-laying. In most cases she bores into the ground with the ovipositor (Ensifera) or the whole abdominal tip (Caelifera). While the crickets and bush-crickets lay their eggs loosely in small clusters or singly, the grasshoppers and ground-hoppers cover their eggs with a quick-setting frothy secretion. In the ground-hoppers they are clumped together with a 'stalk', so that they look like a small bunch of bananas. Some bush-crickets lay their eggs in sites above ground-level, e.g., cracked tree-bark or plant-stems. The Sickle-bearing Bush-cricket lays its flat eggs between the upper and lower surfaces of leaves (*p. 24*, above left). The only northern European grasshoppers to lay their eggs above ground-level are the gold grasshoppers (apart from species that lay their egg-pods in the base of grass-tufts). The Large Gold Grasshopper lays its eggs in broken-off woody plant-stems (*p. 19*, above; *p. 24*, above right). Its small relative folds leaves together and attaches its egg-pods between them (*p. 24*, below right).

Overleaf: Development of *Tettigonia viridissima* (♀), (Ingstetten BS), scale lines 1cm

p. 28, above left, first nymphal instar, May
above right, second nymphal instar, May
below left, third nymphal instar, June
below right, fourth nymphal instar, June

p. 29, above left, fifth nymphal instar, June
above right, sixth nymphal instar, July
below left, seventh nymphal instar, July
below right, adult, July

Nymphal Development

The nymphs hatch in the spring from eggs that have overwintered (only the crickets and ground-hoppers overwinter mainly in other stages); they closely resemble the adults, even in their first instar. Grasshoppers and ground-hoppers have four or five, bush-crickets five to seven and crickets sometimes more than ten nymphal instars. At first, only tiny rudiments of the wings are visible. Only in the last two nymphal instars are the wing rudiments clearly visible as flap-like structures. At first sight these instars could easily be confused with short-winged adults. However, the nymphal hind wing-pads are always broadened into a fan-shape and lie over the fore wing-pads; the two pairs of wing-pads often lie very close together. In short-winged adults, on the other hand, the fore wing always covers the narrowly folded-up hind wings. The long ovipositor of the bush-crickets develops quite gradually, roughly doubling its length from one instar to the next (*pp. 28, 29*). In the first instar, however, it can be seen only with a microscope, and in the last one it has already reached its full length. In many cases, particularly in the bush-crickets, it is possible to identify the species even in the first nymphal instar. Identification keys are available for this purpose (Oschmann 1969, Ingrisch 1977), but they are not quite complete.

Moulting

The nymphs have to moult from time to time in order to grow. Between the moults only the abdomen grows larger, through the intersegmental membrane (which connects the individual segments) becoming increasingly stretched. It is not very easy to observe a moult, as Orthoptera can moult at any time of the day. There are, however, some signs of an impending moult. I shall describe the last moult of *Tettigonia cantans*, the Upland Green Bush-cricket (*pp. 32, 33*).

One or two days before the moult, feeding stops and the wing-pads become clearly separate from the body. A few hours beforehand, air gets under the old nymphal skin, so that it becomes cloudy and whitish. Then the bush-cricket attaches itself firmly to a plant, head downwards. The skin on the top of the pronotum bursts open and the insect slides slowly out of the now transparent covering. There is some difficulty in extricating the long hind legs; the femora, still soft, are bent (*p. 32*, below right) to facilitate the freeing of the tibiae. Soon afterwards they are completely straight again. The antennae also moult over their entire length. When the bush-cricket is completely free from the shed skin, the wings, still soft, are expanded by pumping blood into the wing-veins. When the expanded wings are finally hardened, the hind wings are folded up underneath the fore wings. Finally the bush-cricket eats the shed skin (*p. 33*, below right). In the case described here the whole moulting process up to the eating of the skin took 75 mins.

Although the green bush-crickets emerge from the nymphal skin almost with their final colouring, newly-moulted grasshoppers are white to yellowish at first, and they do not eat the discarded skin. Field-crickets leave their earth burrows to moult. They moult just in front of the burrow entrance by emerging forwards from the skin, which is firmly anchored to the ground.

Overleaf: Last moult in *Tettigonia cantans* (♂), (Pfullingen SA), August
p. 32, above left, the nymphal skin has loosened (08.30 hours);
above right, the bush-cricket slides out of the skin;
below left, the wings are free;
below right, the fore and mid legs are free, the hind femora bent;

p. 33, above left, the legs and antennae are free;
above right, the bush-cricket is completely out of the skin;
below left, the wings are folded but not yet closed together;
below right, the skin is eaten (09.45 hours).

Enemies

Like most insects, Orthoptera are exposed to many predators. A large number are eaten by birds, spiders and other insectivores. In addition to unspecialized predators, there is also a range of enemies specifically committed to Orthoptera.

Among the flies are some conopid and tachinid parasites of Orthoptera – true parasitoids as they kill their host. They attack mainly grasshoppers, laying eggs on their bodies. The fly larvae penetrate into the interior of the body and eventually consume their victim from the inside.

Among the wasps are some sand-wasps (family Sphecidae) that are specialized hunters of Orthoptera. They catch their quarries and paralyse them with a sting into the nervous system. Then they carry them (partly in flight) into a hole previously dug in the ground and lay their eggs on them. Several Orthoptera are usually carried in as food for one wasp larva. Orthoptera-hunters of this kind include several species of the genus *Tachysphex* and *Sphex maxillosus* (*p. 39*, above).

In damp areas many Orthoptera fall victim to the parasitic nematodes of the genera *Mermis* and *Gordius*. These grow inside them into very thin worms, often 20cm long, and survive in water after the death of their hosts.

Many Orthoptera are killed by fungus, especially in wet years. One then sees the apparently intact insects sitting on plants, and only on closer inspection is the fungal growth visible on the lifeless body (*p. 39*, below).

By contrast, the generally parasitic mites of the family Trombidiidae are harmless. Their red larvae, unsegmented and sack-like, suck blood through the intersegmental membrane, often, for example, under the wings. They appear not to harm their hosts materially. They later moult into eight-legged mites, which live predaceously on the ground.

Conservation

Many species of Orthoptera are today endangered through environmental changes. It is not only the strikingly-coloured species that have declined in recent years, but also some of the less spectacular ones. Particularly hard-hit are those with very narrow habitat requirements, such as the gravel-bank species. Many species occurring in areas affected by agriculture, and most of those living in damp places, have also become rarer. The decline of species needing warm, dry conditions is also disturbing.

In some countries lists of endangered species have been prepared ('Red Data Lists') and laws have been enacted to forbid the collection of particular species. Collecting is sometimes necessary, however, in order to provide definite proof of the occurrence of such species. Without the collectors of the past we should be unable to demonstrate today the disappearance of many species from some areas (through changes in the habitats, it should be noted, and not because of collectors!). It is a widespread misconception, especially in conservation circles, that insect collectors contribute to the decline of species. Only in most exceptional cases can this be true.

The British Orthoptera

Of the 78 species described in this book, only 29 occur in the British Isles, and only about 10 of these are at all common and widespread, even in Southern England. Indeed, three of the British species, *Decticus verrucivorus* (Wart-biter), *Gryllus campestris* (Field-cricket) and *Gryllotalpa gryllotalpa* (Mole-cricket), all common in continental Europe, have become so rare here that they are in danger of extinction. Only eight species occur in Scotland and about 10 in Ireland.

The main reason for our impoverished fauna lies in our history since the last Ice Age, during which no Orthoptera were able to exist in the tundra-like conditions of northern Europe. As the climate improved, the more cold-tolerant species spread northwards again, and reached the British Isles (perhaps about 12,000 years ago) while they still formed part of continental Europe. However, soon after this (some 10,000 years ago), the English Channel was formed by the rising sea and no further species were able to reach Britain from the Continent. There is little doubt that a number of the species now occurring in Germany and the Low Countries, but not in the British Isles, would flourish here if they had not been prevented from reaching us by the English Channel.

Within the British Isles, our Orthoptera fauna is richest in southern England, and especially so in the New Forest and Isle of Purbeck. The New Forest provides the main British strongholds of *Nemobius sylvestris* (Wood-cricket) in the woodland, and *Stethophyma grossum* (Large Marsh Grasshopper) in the wettest bogs. Our only known localities for *Chorthippus vagans* (Heath Grasshopper) are on dry heathland in the western part of the Forest and northern Purbeck. The extreme south of England also provides the only British localities for *Conocephalus discolor* (Long-winged Cone-head), *Decticus verrucivorus* (Wart-biter), *Gryllus campestris* (Field-cricket), *Pseudomogoplistes squamiger* (known only from Chesil Beach and not described in this book) and *Gryllotalpa gryllotalpa* (Mole-cricket).

A list of the British Orthoptera, roughly classified according to their distribution, is given below.

Widespread in the British Isles

Acheta domesticus (House-cricket) (indoors or on refuse tips)
Tetrix undulata (Common Ground-hopper)
Omocestus viridulus (Common Green Grasshopper)
Myrmeleotettix maculatus Mottled Grasshopper)
Chorthippus brunneus (Field Grasshopper)

Occurring in southern Britain and Ireland, but absent or rare in Scotland

Leptophyes punctatissima (Speckled Bush-cricket)
Meconema thalassinum (Oak Bush-cricket)
Metrioptera roeselii (Roesel's Bush-cricket)
Pholidoptera griseoaptera (Dark Bush-cricket)
Tetrix subulata (Slender Ground-hopper)
Stethophyma grossum (Large Marsh Grasshopper)
Chorthippus albomarginatus (Lesser Marsh Grasshopper)

Widespread in Britain, but absent from Ireland

Tachycines asynamorus (Greenhouse Camel-cricket) (in greenhouses)
Chorthippus parallelus (Meadow Grasshopper)

Fairly widespread in southern Britain; absent from Ireland

Conocephalus dorsalis (Short-winged Cone-head)
Tettigonia viridissima (Great Green Bush-cricket)
Platycleis albopunctata (Grey Bush-cricket)
Metrioptera brachyptera (Bog Bush-cricket)
Tetrix ceperoi (Cepero's Ground-hopper)
Stenobothrus lineatus (Stripe-winged Grasshopper)
Omocestus rufipes (Woodland Grasshopper)
Gomphocerippus rufus (Rufous Grasshopper)

Known only from the Isle of Man

Stenobothrus stigmaticus (Lesser Mottled Grasshopper)

Very local in southern England

Conocephalus discolor (Long-winged Cone-head)
Decticus verrucivorus (Wart-biter)
Gryllus campestris (Field-cricket)
Nemobius sylvestrus (Wood-cricket)
Pseudomogoplistes squamiger (Scaly cricket)
Gryllotalpa gryllotalpa (Mole-cricket)
Chorthippus vagans (Heath Grasshopper)

Overleaf: *p. 38*, Long-winged forms of usually short-winged Orthoptera
above, *Metrioptera roeselii* ♀, (Schwaigfurt OS), July
below, *Chrysochraon dispar* ♀, Baustetten OS, July

p. 39, Enemies and diseases of Orthoptera
above, sand-wasp (*Sphex maxillosus*) with a captured bush-cricket, a Mediterranean meconematine (*Cyrtaspis scutata*), Scarlino Tu, September
below, Rufous Grasshopper (*Gomphocerippus rufus*) killed by fungus

Collecting and Keeping Alive

In many cases Orthoptera can be recognized from a distance. However, it is often necessary to catch them in order to identify the species reliably. This can best be achieved with a short-handled net, which can be made out of bent wire and light net-curtain material. The diameter should be about 20cm, so that the net can be easily packed.

For some species, particularly the Oak Bush-cricket, a 'beating umbrella' is very useful. This corresponds roughly in shape and size to a white inverted umbrella without a shaft. The beating umbrella is held under a branch, which is then tapped lightly with a stick. Many insects and spiders, including Oak Bush-crickets 'sleeping' during the day under leaves, fall on to the white cloth, where they are easily seen.

If it is possible to make a reliable identification on the spot, the insects can be released again. For preparing a faunal inventory or if identification in the field is uncertain, however, it is sensible to take away a pair of each species for preparation at home, to confirm the identification and also to have voucher specimens. In addition, the keeping of livestock under laboratory conditions offers many opportunities for observation. Most of the species can be carried in 40ml glass phials with snap-on lids; large Orthoptera can be carried in jam-jars (always singly!).

Nymphs and smaller species can be kept alive in jam-jars with perforated lids, but they should then be kept singly. If one intends to keep several insects together, a large terrarium is necessary, such as a plastic aquarium tank with a gauze cover. Food can be (depending on the species) oatmeal, chopped-up mealworms and various plants, such as dandelion, chickweed and grasses. Many bush-crickets like to feed on aphid-covered plant stems. Another good food is freshly germinated wheat, which can be grown in flowerpots.

Many species can be reared from the nymph without difficulty. The songs and the mating behaviour of the adults can be studied in the terrarium. In order to observe mating the sexes must be kept separate for a time (preferably the last nymphal instar). Putting the males and females together then usually succeeds at first attempt. However, many crickets and bush-crickets mate only in the evening and at night.

To study the songs of grasshoppers it is best to put several males together and warm the terrarium with a 60W lamp placed about 30cm away. Under such conditions nearly all grasshoppers sing at any time during the day or night, producing the calling and rivalry songs. It is nevertheless necessary in some species to isolate a single male in order to obtain the calling song in a pure form. To hear the courtship song a female must be added. The crickets and bush-crickets usually sing without artificial lighting, many of them only during darkness.

Killing insects for no definite purpose must be avoided, but it is sometimes necessary to kill *Chorthippus* and *Tetrix* species, for example, in order to study them in detail.

Place the insects in a tightly closed jam-jar with some cellulose tissue and a few drops of ethyl acetate; they should be removed only after about an hour (otherwise they sometimes recover). To produce good specimens, Ensifera and large Caelifera are best eviscerated. For this purpose an incision is made in the upper neck membrane (especially in Caelifera) or along the underside of the abdomen, a little to one side of the middle, using a pair of fine dissecting scissors. The whole of the gut is then removed through the incision with a pair of fine forceps. The resulting cavity is then stuffed with a rolled cottonwool plug. In the smaller Caelifera (about the size of *Chorthippus*) evisceration is unnecessary. The specimen is then pinned (with an entomological pin) through the pronotum. After that green bush-crickets are immersed for about 30 mins in an acetone bath in order to preserve the colour. Finally the legs and antennae are straightened out on a polystyrene block (which has to be covered with paper when using acetone-treated specimens) and held in position with pins until dry. In the grasshoppers it is sensible to spread the wings on one side so as to be able to see the wing-venation. For this one can use small pieces of bevelled balsa wood (obtainable from model shops) cut to a suitable size and fastened (e.g., with adhesive tape) next to the specimen on the polystyrene block. Then the wings are spread out and fastened securely to the wood with pins and transparent paper. Always note the locality data on a small label and later add this to the pin.

Photographing and Tape-recording

In recent years photographing insects has clearly become more important than collecting them. We must never forget, however, that the documentary evidence of a photograph has limitations. Even a very good habitus-shot of an *Oedipoda*, for example, cannot show whether it is the red-winged or blue-winged species. In most cases, however, it is possible to 'collect' and reliably identify Orthoptera in the form of photographs.

I have taken almost all the photographs shown in this book with a small single-lens reflex camera (Asahi Pentax) with a 100mm macro lens. The use, in addition, of a bellows (Novoflex) and/or extension tubes allowed the image/object ratio to reach 2.3:1 – more than double natural size. This was sufficient for almost all the species. Only for the Ant-cricket was an even larger magnification necessary (3:1, by means of a 55mm lens in reverse position on the bellows).

For a light source I used two battery flashes of light number 20, fixed at the side of the lens. In one case (egg of *Phaneroptera*) they were positioned to give cross-lighting. The film used was Kodachrome 25, which undoubtedly gives the best definition.

For flight photographs other equipment is necessary. For triggering I used a light cabinet (Bergtron) with a focusable light-pointer. In order to achieve an acceptable success rate in relation to film consumption, a larger format is essential. I used a 6×6 single-lens reflex camera with central shutter (Zenza Bronica). The flashes were the same as in the other photographs. The film was Ektachrome 64.

The flight photographs were taken indoors. In the remaining cases I tried to photograph the insects under as natural conditions as possible in the open. For the photographs that were taken in the open but not at the original locality, I have cited the locality in parentheses.

Tape-recordings provide a good means of committing the songs of Orthoptera to memory. Making recordings of Orthoptera in a terrarium generally presents no difficulties. One need only position the microphone close enough to the insect (within about 10–20cm). Recordings of bush-crickets are more difficult. The higher-pitched sounds are frequently distorted, especially when the microphone distance is too small. Such recordings can be further 'adjusted' with a frequency-corrector (equalizer). One can, for example, suppress all frequencies below 4kHz and thus obtain very clean recordings of sounds with frequencies above that level.

Identification Key Based on Structural Characters

In most cases this key will enable the living insect to be identified; in some cases (as in some *Chorthippus* and *Tetrix* species) identification is rather uncertain without a prepared specimen. A good lens (about ×10 magnification) is generally sufficient. Identification from photographs is, however, not always possible with this key, as the diagnostic characters (e.g., the cerci) are often not visible. NB: long-winged individuals of usually short-winged species are disregarded in the key; they are, however, very much rarer than the similar-looking normal insects. In order to save space, the key sometimes departs from the strictly dichotomous principle (choice between number and dash) and puts two alternatives (– and —) with a number.

I–1
Gryllotalpa gryllotalpa: right fore leg

(**I** followed by a number refers the reader to the drawings illustrating structural characters.)

1. Fore legs developed into digging legs (I–1). Unable to jump.
   Gryllotalpa gryllotalpa, p. 124

– Fore legs normal. Usually able to jump. 2

2. Antennae as long as the body or longer (Ensifera). 3

– Antennae shorter than the body (Caelifera). 32

3. Smaller than 5mm. Wings and hearing organs absent.
   Myrmecophilus acervorum, p. 122

– Larger than 5mm. 4

4. Wings and hearing organs completely absent. Only in greenhouses.
   Tachycines asynamorus, p. 114

– At least vestiges of wings and hearing organs (on the fore knee) present. 5

I–2
Gryllus campestris: right fore tarsus

5. Tarsi three-segmented (I–2), insect never green (crickets). 6

I–3
Metrioptera roeselii: right fore tarsus

– Tarsi four-segmented (I–3), insect often green (bush-crickets). 10

6. Colouring dark brown to black. 7

– Colouring pale brown or yellowish. 9

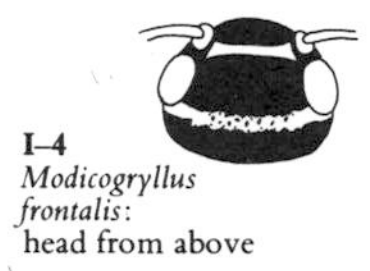
I–4
Modicogryllus frontalis: head from above

7. Body-length at least 20mm, colouring black. *Gryllus campestris, p. 116*

– Body-length under 20mm. 8

8. Body-length 12–13mm. Whitish-yellow transverse band in front of the eyes (I–4). *Modicogryllus frontalis, p. 118*

I–5
Nemobius sylvestris: head from above

– Body-length 7–10mm. White line in the form of a pentagon in front of the eyes (I–5). *Nemobius sylvestris, p. 120*

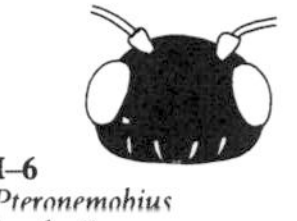
I–6
Pteronemobius heydenii: head from above

– Body-length 6–7mm. Pale longitudinal lines behind the eyes (I–6). *Pteronemobius heydenii, p. 112*

9. Head yellow-brown with black transverse bands. *Acheta domesticus, p. 118*

– Head yellow-brown with two black longitudinal lines behind the eyes. *Oecanthus pellucens, p. 124*

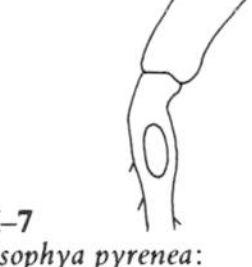
I–7
Isophya pyrenea: right fore knee

10. Tympanal opening round (I–7). 11

– Tympanal opening slit-like (I–8). 19

11. Wings fully developed. 12

– Wings shortened. 13

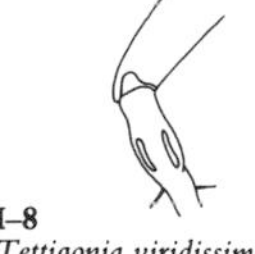
I–8
Tettigonia viridissima: right fore knee

12. Fore wings shorter than the hind wings. *Phaneroptera falcata, p. 72*

– Fore and hind wings the same length. *Meconema thalassinum, p. 86*

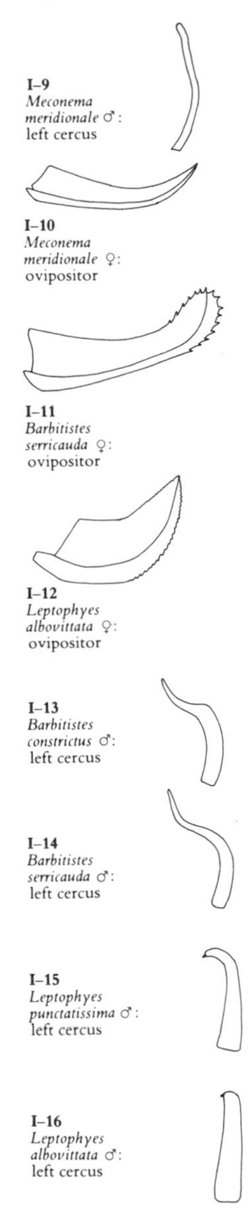

I–9 *Meconema meridionale* ♂: left cercus

I–10 *Meconema meridionale* ♀: ovipositor

I–11 *Barbitistes serricauda* ♀: ovipositor

I–12 *Leptophyes albovittata* ♀: ovipositor

I–13 *Barbitistes constrictus* ♂: left cercus

I–14 *Barbitistes serricauda* ♂: left cercus

I–15 *Leptophyes punctatissima* ♂: left cercus

I–16 *Leptophyes albovittata* ♂: left cercus

13. ♂: cerci as in I–9. ♀: ovipositor sword-shaped (I–10).
Meconema meridionale, p. 86

– ♂: cerci as in I–13 to I–16. ♀: ovipositor coarsely toothed (I–11) or short and sickle-shaped (I–12). 14

14. Antennae more than twice as long as the body (without ovipositor). 15

– Antennae less than twice as long as the body. 18

15. ♂: cerci S-shaped (I–13). ♀: ovipositor coarsely toothed (I–11). 16

– ♂: cerci curved simply like a hook (I–15, I–16). ♀: ovipositor very finely toothed (use a lens!), short and sickle-shaped (I–12). 17

16. ♂: cerci somewhat broadened before the tip (I–13). ♀: ovipositor at least 2.5 times as long as the pronotum.
Barbitistes constrictus, p. 78

– ♂: cerci not broadened (I–14). ♀: ovipositor at most slightly more than twice as long as the pronotum.
Barbitistes serricauda, p. 76

17. ♂: cerci curved in the distal third (I–15). ♀: ovipositor more than twice as long as the pronotum.
Leptophyes punctatissima, p. 82

– ♂: cerci quite straight with an inwardly curved apical tooth (I–16). ♀: ovipositor slightly longer than the pronotum.
Leptophyes albovittata, p. 80

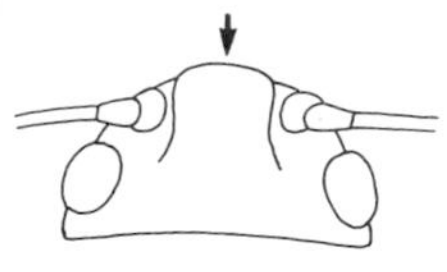

I–17
Polysarcus denticauda:
head from above

18. Tip of the vertex between the antennae broader than the first antennal segment (I–17). *Polysarcus denticauda, p. 84*

– Tip of the vertex narrower than the first antennal segment (I–18). *Isophya pyrenea, p. 74*

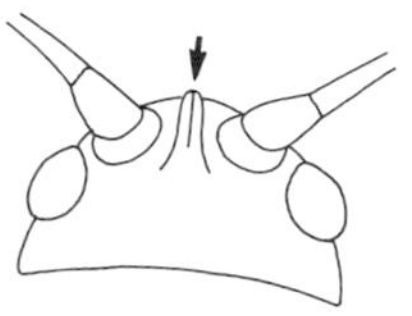

I–18
Isophya pyrenea:
head from above

19. Head noticeably pointed at the front (I–19, I–20). 20

– Head not noticeably pointed at the front (I–21), often simply rounded. 21

20. Body-length at least 20mm. Wings extending well beyond the hind knees. *Ruspolia nitidula, p. 90*

– Body-length under 20mm. Wings extending slightly beyond the hind knees. *Conocephalus discolor, p. 88*

— Body-length under 20mm. Wings extending to about the middle of the abdomen. *Conocephalus dorsalis, p. 90*

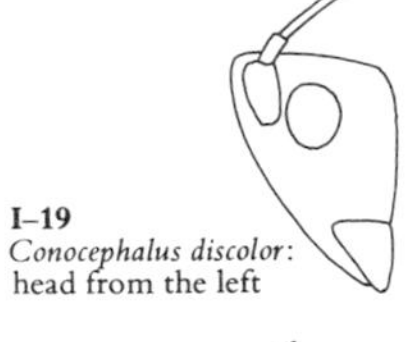

I–19
Conocephalus discolor:
head from the left

I–20
Ruspolia nitidula:
head from the left

21. Top of the pronotum with a clear angle in side view (I 22). *Ephippiger ephippiger, p. 112*

– Top of the pronotum flat or slightly arched (I–23). 22

22. Colouring almost uniformly green, only the back and legs often yellowish to brownish. Body-size at least 20mm. 23

– Colouring green or brown; green insects either under 20mm or strongly mottled, usually with dark, square spots on the fore wings 25

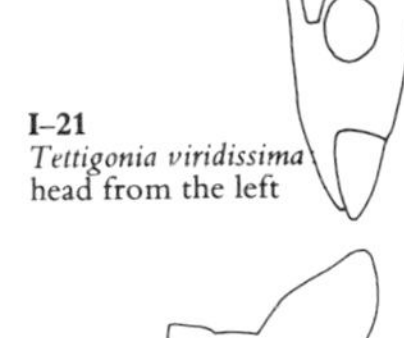

I–21
Tettigonia viridissima
head from the left

I–22
Ephippiger ephippiger:
pronotum from the left

23. Wings reaching about as far as the hind knees. *Tettigonia cantans, p. 94*

– Wings extending clearly beyond the hind knees. 24

I–23
Pholidoptera griseoaptera:
pronotum from the left

I–24
Tettigonia viridissima ♂: cerci with the subgenital plate and styles from below

24. ♂: cerci much longer than the styles (I–24). ♀: ovipositor reaching about as far as the wing-tips.
Tettigonia viridissima, p. 92

– ♂: cerci and styles almost the same length (I–25). ♀: ovipositor extending well beyond the wing-tips. Only in eastern Europe. *Tettigonia caudata, p. 94*

I–25
Tettigonia caudata ♂: cerci with the subgenital plate and styles from below

25. Fore wings extending beyond the tip of the abdomen, usually with dark, square spots. 26

– Fore wings shorter than the abdomen, without spots. 29

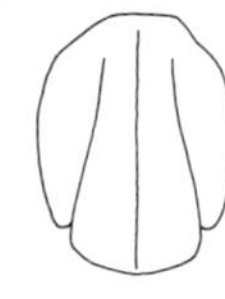

I–26
Decticus verrucivorus: pronotum from above

26. Pronotum with a median keel throughout its length (I–26). Body-length 24–44mm. Ground-colour green or brown.
Decticus verrucivorus, p. 96

– Pronotum without a median keel (I–27). Body-length 20–26mm. Ground-colour green, rarely yellowish.
Gampsocleis glabra, p. 98

I–27
Gampsocleis glabra: pronotum from above

27. Wings reaching about as far as the hind knees. *Platycleis albopunctata, p. 100*

– Wings shorter. 28

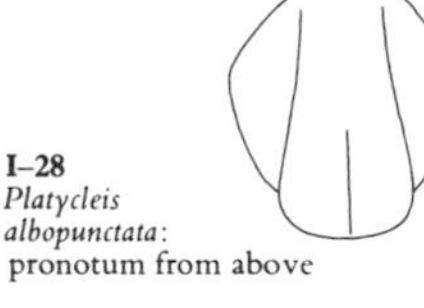

I–28
Platycleis albopunctata: pronotum from above

28. ♂: cerci toothed at the base (I–29). ♀: ovipositor weakly curved (I–30). Only in eastern Europe.
Platycleis montana, p. 102

– ♂: cerci toothed near the tip (I–31). ♀: ovipositor strongly curved (I–32).
Platycleis tessellata, p. 102

I–29
Platycleis montana ♂: right cercus

I–30
Platycleis montana ♀:
ovipositor

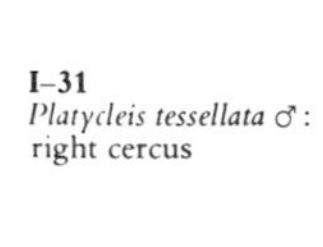

I–31
Platycleis tessellata ♂:
right cercus

I–32
Platycleis tessellata ♀:
ovipositor

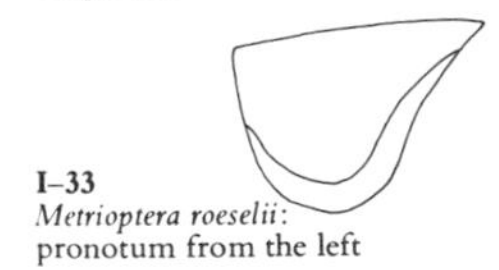

I–33
Metrioptera roeselii:
pronotum from the left

I–34
Metrioptera brachyptera:
pronotum from the left

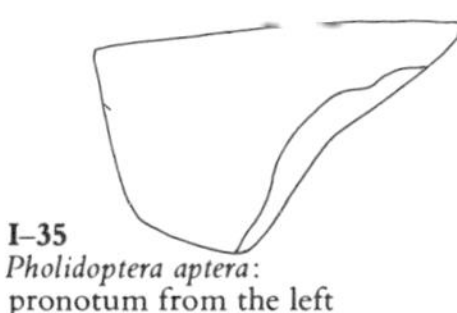

I–35
Pholidoptera aptera:
pronotum from the left

I–36
Pholidoptera griseoaptera:
pronotum from the left

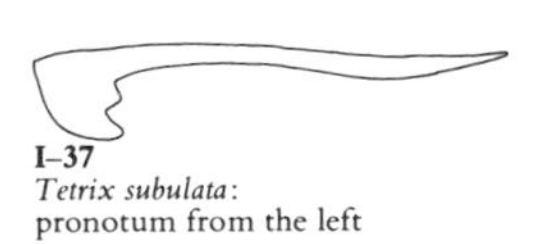

I–37
Tetrix subulata:
pronotum from the left

29. Fore wings clearly longer than the pronotum in the male, slightly longer in the female. 30

– Fore wings slightly shorter than the pronotum in the male, clearly shorter in the female. 31

30. Pronotal side-flaps dark, with a broad pale green or whitish border below and behind (I–33).
Metrioptera roeselii, p. 104

– Pronotal side-flaps dark, with a narrow white border behind only (I–34), sometimes indistinct.
Metrioptera brachyptera, p. 106

— Pronotal side-flaps uniformly pale green or pale brown.
Metrioptera bicolor, p. 106

31. Pronotal side-flaps with a broad, sharply-defined, pale border behind (I–35). *Pholidoptera aptera, p. 108*

– Pronotal side-flaps with a quite narrow and usually indistinct pale border behind (I–36).
Pholidoptera griseoaptera, p. 110

32. Pronotum extended backwards into a long spike reaching at least to the tip of the abdomen (I–37, I–42). 33

– Pronotum without such a spike. 38

33. Keel along the back of the pronotum hardly arched, almost straight in side view (I–37). 34

– Keel along the back of the pronotum clearly arched (I–42, I–44). 36

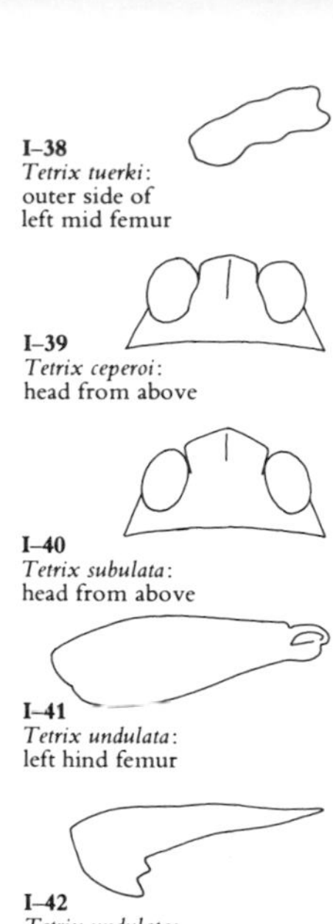

I–38
Tetrix tuerki:
outer side of
left mid femur

I–39
Tetrix ceperoi:
head from above

I–40
Tetrix subulata:
head from above

I–41
Tetrix undulata:
left hind femur

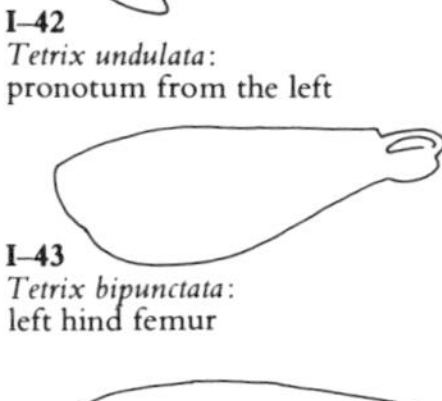

I–42
Tetrix undulata:
pronotum from the left

I–43
Tetrix bipunctata:
left hind femur

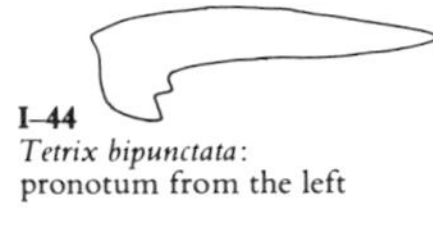

I–44
Tetrix bipunctata:
pronotum from the left

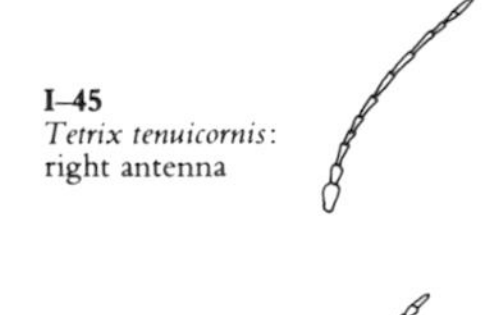

I–45
Tetrix tenuicornis:
right antenna

I–46
Tetrix bipunctata:
right antenna

34. Mid femora clearly wavy below (I–38). *Tetrix tuerki, p. 128*

– Mid femora not wavy below. (It is very difficult to distinguish between the following two species.) 35

35. Vertex between the eyes, seen from above, about as wide as one eye and hardly extending forwards beyond the eyes (I–39). (Rare species.) *Tetrix ceperoi, p. 128*

– Vertex between the eyes wider than one eye and clearly extending forwards beyond the eyes (I–40). *Tetrix subulata, p. 126*

36. Hind femora about three times as long as broad (I–41). Keel along the back of the pronotum less strongly arched (I–42). *Tetrix undulata, p. 130*

– Hind femora less than three times as long as broad (I–43). Keel along the back of the pronotum strongly arched (I–44). 37

37. Antennae long and slender, middle segments about four times as long as broad (I–45). *Tetrix tenuicornis, p. 130*

– Antennae short and thick, middle segments about twice as long as broad (I–46). *Tetrix bipunctata, p. 132*

38. A clearly visible, cylindrical spine present between the fore coxae (I–47). 39

– No such spine present between the fore coxae, but sometimes a smaller conical protuberance (I–50) (use a lens!). 41

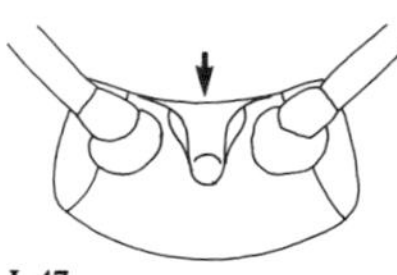

I–47
Calliptamus italicus:
prosternum

39. Wings fully developed, hind wings pink towards the base.
Calliptamus italicus, p. 138

– Wings shortened. 40

40. Ground-colour brown, hind tibiae bluish. *Podisma pedestris, p. 134*

– Ground-colour green, hind tibiae yellow or red. *Miramella alpina, p. 136*

41. Hind wings partly red, pink or pale blue. 42

– Hind wings not coloured, but sometimes wholly or partly dark brown. 46

42. Pronotum with a high median keel throughout. Hind wings red. Male flies with a loud rattle.
Psophus stridulus, p. 140

– Median keel of pronotum interrupted by one or more transverse grooves.
43

43. Hind femora with a clear step above (I–48, I–49). 44

– Hind femora not stepped above. 45

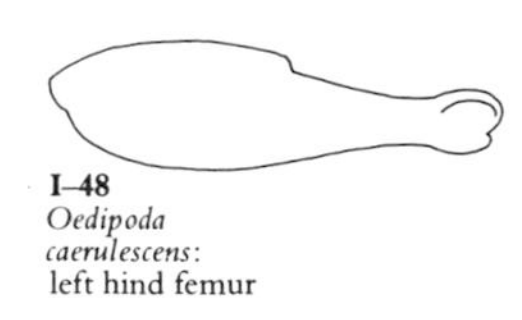

I–48
Oedipoda caerulescens:
left hind femur

44. Hind wings blue. Step very clear (I–48). *Oedipoda caerulescens, p. 144*

– Hind wings red. Step rather less sharply defined (I–49).
Oedipoda germanica, p. 146

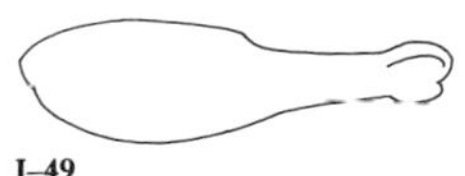

I–49
Oedipoda germanica:
left hind femur

45. Hind wings pale red towards the base. Hind tibiae yellow. Flies with a whirring sound.
Bryodema tuberculata, p. 148

– Hind wings pale blue towards the base. Hind tibiae bluish.
Sphingonotus caerulans, p. 150

46. Larger than 30mm. Green, brown or yellowish; fore wings with dark square spots or unspotted.
Locusta migratoria, p. 142

– Smaller than 30mm. If larger, then fore wings with a yellowish stripe near the anterior margin. 47

47. Pronotal side-keels absent or only weakly developed in the posterior half. 48

– Pronotal side-keels present. 50

48. Sides of the pronotum with a sharply defined black longitudinal band.
Mecostethus alliaceus, p. 156

– Sides of the pronotum without a black band. 49

49. Hind tibiae reddish (sometimes yellowish). Fore wings with large, dark spots. *Aiolopus thalassinus, p. 152*

– Hind tibiae bluish. Fore wings with smaller, darker speckling.
Epacromius tergestinus, p. 152

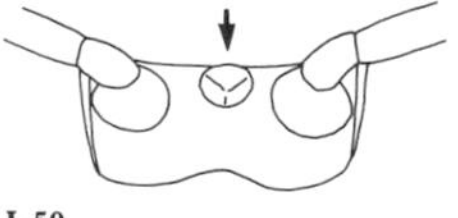

I–50
Stethophyma grossum: prosternum

50. Hind femora red below, knees black. Hind tibiae yellow or red. Fore wings with a yellowish longitudinal stripe. A small conical protuberance present between the fore coxae (I–50) (difficult to see). 51

– Hind femora not red below. If they are, then fore wings without a yellow longitudinal stripe. No protuberance present between the fore coxae. 53

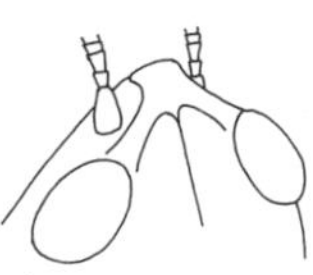

I–51
Chrysochraon dispar:
vertex obliquely from above

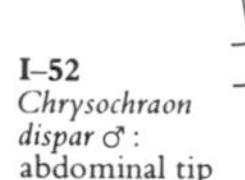

I–52
Chrysochraon dispar ♂:
abdominal tip

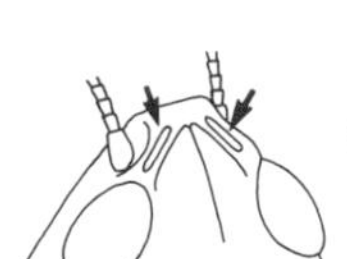

I–53
Omocestus viridulus:
vertex obliquely from above

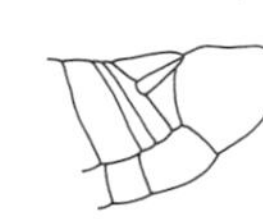

I–54
Chorthippus biguttulus ♂:
abdominal tip

I–55
Chysochraon brachypterus ♂:
right fore wing

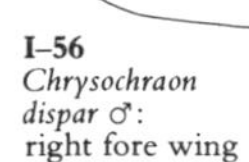

I–56
Chrysochraon dispar ♂:
right fore wing

I–57
Gomphocerus sibiricus ♂:
antennal tip

51. Hind tibiae yellow with black spines.
Stethophyma grossum, p. 154

– Hind tibiae red. 52

52. Hind wings blackish brown. Pronotal side-keels gently incurved (but with angled yellow stripes along them). Male rattles in flight.
Arcyptera fusca, p. 158

– Hind wings transparent. Pronotal side-keels angled.
Arcyptera microptera, p. 156

53. Foveolae absent (I–51). Male abdomen with pointed tip (I–52). Wings greatly shortened in the female, at most not quite reaching the tip of the abdomen in the male. 54

– Foveolae present (I–53), but sometimes indistinct. Male abdomen with rounded tip (I–54). 55

54. Both sexes metallic green. Male with pale hind knees and truncate, slightly emarginate fore wings reaching halfway along the abdomen (I–55). Female with pink or greenish fore wing scales, which are widely separated on the back.
Chrysochraon brachypterus, p. 162

– ♂: metallic wings with dark knees and rounded fore wings almost reaching the tip of the abdomen (I–56). ♀: brown with brown fore wing scales, which almost touch on the back.
Chrysochraon dispar, p. 160

55. Antennae somewhat broadened at the tip (I–57) (seen from above). 56

– Antennae not broadened. 58

I–58
Gomphocerippus rufus:
right fore wing

56. Fore wings without a bulge on the anterior margin.
Myrmeleotettix maculatus, p. 180

– Fore wings with a small bulge on the anterior margin (I–58). 57

I–59
Gomphocerus sibiricus ♂:
right fore leg

57. Antennal clubs with pale tips.
Gomphocerippus rufus, p. 178

– Antennal clubs uniformly dark. Only in high mountains. Male with swollen, bladder-like fore tibiae (I–59).
Gomphocerus sibiricus, p. 176

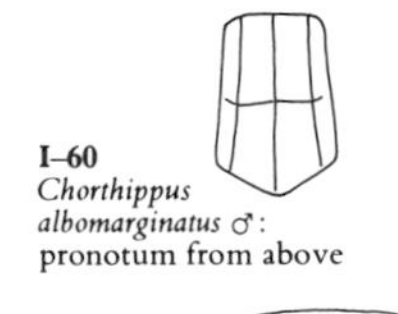

I–60
Chorthippus albomarginatus ♂:
pronotum from above

I–61
Stenobothrus nigromaculatus ♂:
right fore wing
with the medial area

58. Fore wings without a bulge on the anterior margin. 59

– Fore wings with a small bulge on the anterior margin (I–58). 67

59. Pronotal side-keels almost straight, slightly diverging posteriorly (I–60).
Chorthippus albomarginatus ♂, *p. 198*

– Pronotal side-keels incurved (I–65) or angled (I–67). 60

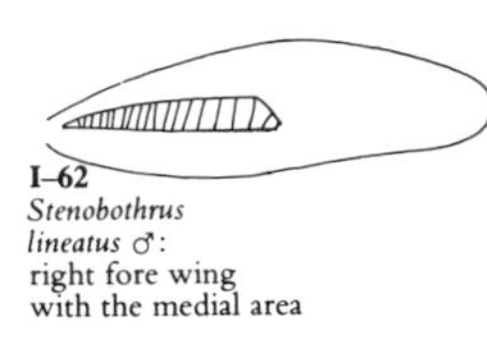

I–62
Stenobothrus lineatus ♂:
right fore wing
with the medial area

I–63
Stenobothrus stigmaticus ♂:
right fore wing
with the medial area

60. Medial area of the fore wings broadened and with regular, parallel veinlets (I–61 to I–63). 61

– Medial area of the fore wing not broadened (I–64). 63

61. Medial area longer than half the length of the fore wing (I–61).
Stenobothrus nigromaculatus, p. 166

– Medial area about half the length of the fore wing (I–62, I–63). 62

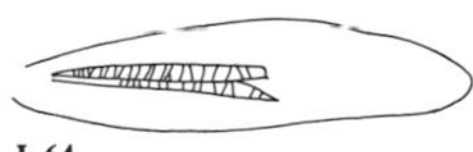

I–64
Omocestus viridulus ♂:
right fore wing
with the medial and
first cubital areas

62. Fore wings more than 3mm wide.
Stenobothrus lineatus, p. 164

– Fore wings less than 3mm wide.
Stenobothrus stigmaticus, p. 168

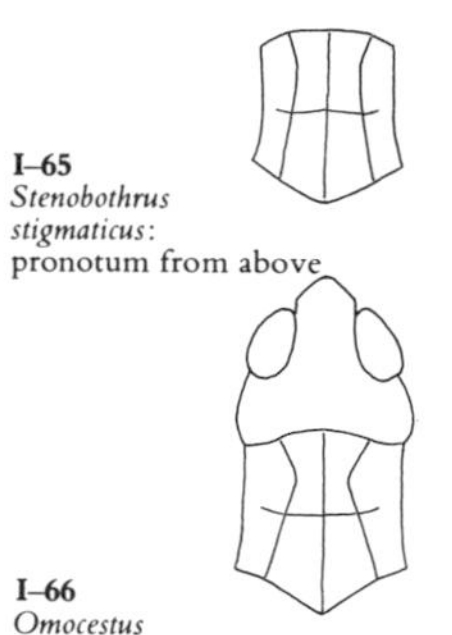

I–65
Stenobothrus stigmaticus:
pronotum from above

I–66
Omocestus haemorrhoidalis:
pronotum and head from above

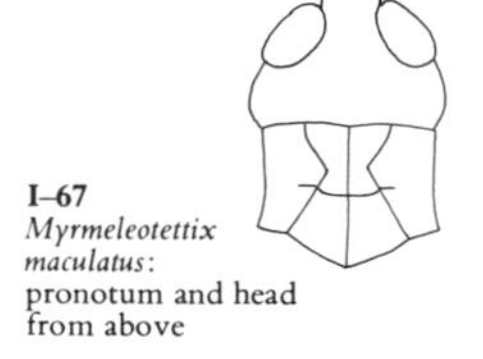

I–67
Myrmeleotettix maculatus:
pronotum and head from above

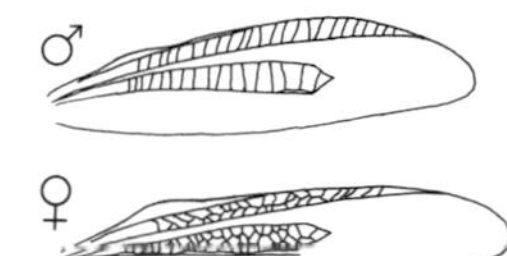

I–68
Chorthippus apricarius ♂ and ♀:
right fore wing with costal and medial areas

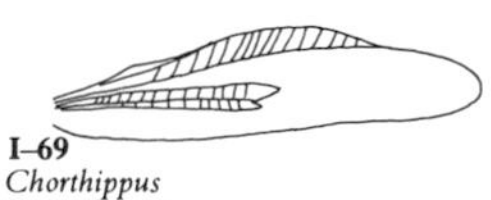

I–69
Chorthippus biguttulus ♂:
right fore wing with costal, medial and first cubital areas

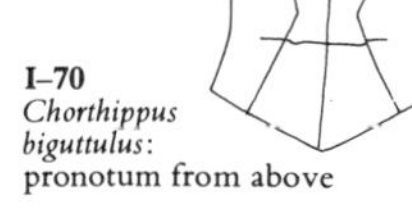

I–70
Chorthippus biguttulus:
pronotum from above

63. Underside of the abdomen conspicuously coloured: green at the front, then yellow and becoming red towards the tip of the abdomen. Palps black with white tips. *Omocestus rufipes, p. 172*

– Underside of the abdomen without such colouring, although the tip of the abdomen is often red. 64

64. Medial area of the fore wings without spots or very indistinctly spotted. Tip of the abdomen never red.
Omocestus viridulus, p. 170

– Medial area of the fore wings with dark spots. 65

65. Pronotal side-keels about 1.5 times further apart at the back than at the narrowest point (I–65).
Stenobothrus stigmaticus, p. 168

– Pronotal side-keels at least twice as far apart at the back as at the narrowest point (I–66, I–67). 66

66. Head, seen from above, shorter than the pronotum (I–66).
Omocestus haemorrhoidalis, p. 174

– Head, seen from above, as long as the pronotum (I–67).
Myrmeleotettix maculatus ♀, p. 180

67. Hind wings uniformly blackish-brown. Rattles in flight.
Stauroderus scalaris, p. 182

– Hind wings paler. 68

68. Medial area broadened, with parallel veinlets in the male and with a network of veinlets in the female (I 68).
Chorthippus apricarius, p. 184

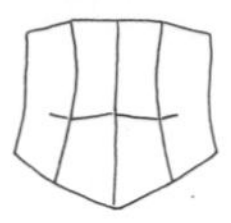

I–71
Chorthippus dorsatus:
pronotum from above

I–72
Chorthippus vagans:
right tympanal
opening

I–73
Chorthippus biguttulus:
right tympanal
opening

– Medial area not broadened (I–69). 69

69. Pronotal side-keels angularly bent (I–70). 70

– Pronotal side-keels parallel at the front, diverging behind (I–71). 73

70. Tympanal opening oval (I–72). 71

– Tympanal opening narrowly kidney-shaped (I–73). 72

71. Wings reaching to about the hind knees, sometimes slightly shorter in the female.
Chorthippus vagans, p. 188

[71 continued at top of p. 57]

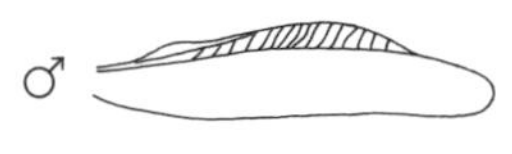

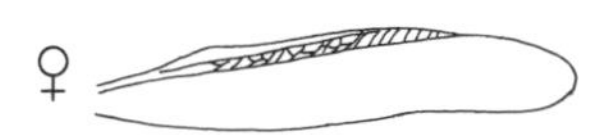

I–74
Chorthippus biguttulus
♂ and ♀:
right fore wing
with costal area

1 cm

♂: L 12, B 3, L/B 4; ♀: L 15, B 3, L/B 5 (I–74). *Chorthippus biguttulus, p. 190*

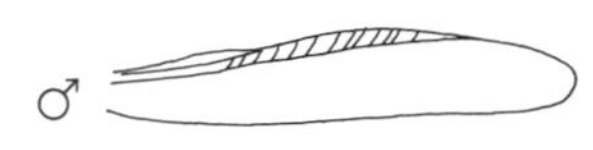

I–75
Chorthippus brunneus
♂ and ♀:
right fore wing
with costal area

1cm

– ♂: L 14.5, B 3, L/B 4.8; ♀: L 18, B 3, L/B 6 (I–75).
Chorthippus brunneus, p. 192

I–76
Chorthippus mollis
♂ and ♀:
right fore wing
with costal area

1cm

— ♂: L 12, B 2.5, L/B 4.8; ♀: L 15, B 2.5, L/B 6 (I–76). *Chorthippus mollis, p. 194*

– Wings reaching to the tip of the abdomen in the male, to the middle of the abdomen in the female.
Chorthippus pullus, p. 186

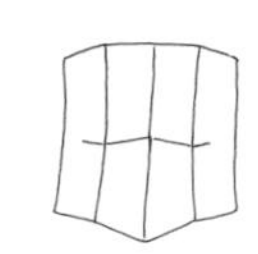

I–77
Chorthippus albomarginatus ♀: pronotum from above

72. Distinguishing the previous three species is difficult, but best achieved on the basis of the shape and size of the fore wings (mean values in mm: L = length, B = breadth). Identification by song is easier!

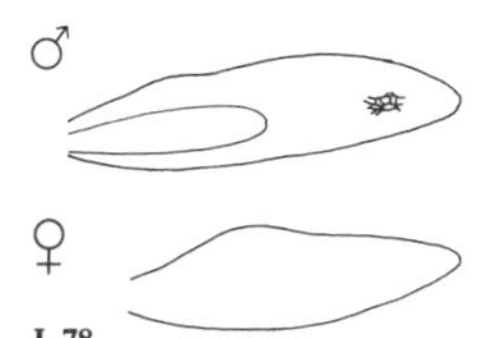

I–78
Chorthippus parallelus ♂ and ♀: right fore wing (in the ♂ with the stigma and outline of the hind wing)

73. Wings fully developed, hind knees pale. 74

– Wings shortened (in the male reaching at most to the tip of the abdomen), hind knees dark. 75

74. Pronotal side-keels almost straight (I–77). Fore wings with a white longitudinal stripe.
Chorthippus albomarginatus, p. 198

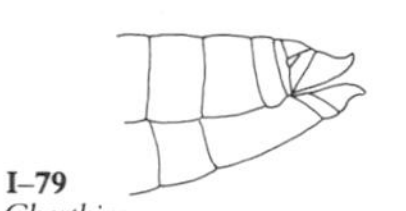

I–79
Chorthippus parallelus ♀: abdominal tip

– Pronotal side-keels clearly incurved (I–71). Fore wings without a white stripe. *Chorthippus dorsatus, p. 196*

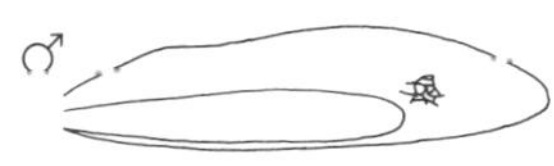

♀

I–80
Chorthippus montanus ♂ and ♀: right fore wing (in the ♂ with the stigma and outline of the hind wing)

75. ♂: stigma at most 1.5mm from the tip of the fore wing, hind wings ending well before this (hold against the light!) (I–78). ♀: fore wings pointed (I–78); ovipositor valves shorter (I–79).
Chorthippus parallelus, p. 200

– ♂: stigma at least 2.5mm from the tip of the fore wing, hind wings almost or completely reaching the stigma (I–80). ♀: fore wings rounded (I–80); ovipositor valves longer (I–81).
Chorthippus montanus, p. 202

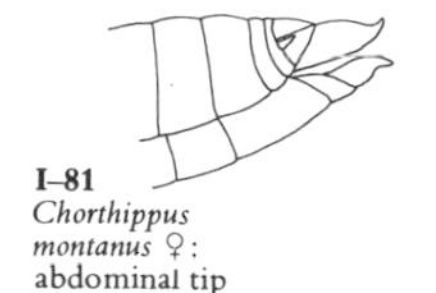

I–81
Chorthippus montanus ♀: abdominal tip

Identification Table of Songs

Many Orthoptera can be identified very easily by their songs, but it is difficult to imagine a particular sound from just a description. In order to make it easily comprehensible, the table includes only the calling songs (and the flight sounds of some species), as these are the sounds most often heard. Other kinds of song, such as rivalry and courtship songs, are much less frequently heard; their inclusion in the table would have made it unwieldy. The sounds produced by the spine-breasted grasshoppers and almost all the Locustinae, which cannot be termed calling songs, are also omitted. So also are a few species, rare in northern Europe, whose songs I have not yet been able to study (*Barbitistes constrictus*, *Gampsocleis glabra*, *Platycleis tessellata*, *Arcyptera microptera*). The song-diagrams should help to clarify the descriptions: they provide additional information, especially on the duration of the songs (the marks under the line indicate the time in seconds). In interpreting these diagrams, as well as the song descriptions, it should be noted that some of the songs can vary greatly according to temperature. All the descriptions relate to temperatures of *c*. 20–30°C. Further details are often given in the species descriptions (*p. 72 ff*).

S followed by a number refers to the song-diagrams.

A Flight sounds (no diagrams)

1. Loud, clearly rattling flight sounds. *Psophus stridulus, p. 140*
2. Loud flight sounds, not rattling. *Bryodema tuberculata, p. 148*
3 & 4. Soft flight sounds. *Arcyptera fusca, p. 158*
Stauroderus scalaris, p. 182

B Longer series of uniform sounds; intervals clearly longer than the sounds

5. Very soft sounds ('tsb') in a rather irregular series (S–1).
Phaneroptera falcata, p. 72

6. Very soft sounds ('tsb') regularly grouped. See under 24

7. Extremely soft sounds ('zb') at 5–10 sec. intervals (S–2).
Leptophyes albovittata, p. 80

8. Extremely soft sounds ('zb') at 3–6 sec. intervals (S–3).
Leptophyes punctatissima, p. 82

9. Irregular sequences of sharp, snapping sounds (S–4).
Stethophyma grossum, p. 154

10. Short, sharp sounds ('st') at intervals of 1–2 sec. (S–5). Alternation singing between two insects frequent. *Chorthippus brunneus, p. 192*

11. Short buzzing sounds of *c.* 0.5 sec. duration ('rrrrt') at intervals of *c.* 2 sec. (S–6). *Chorthippus albomarginatus, p. 198*

12. Loud rasping sounds ('re') in an irregular sequence. See under 40

13. Very short, sharp groups of three syllables, which sound almost like a single syllable. See under 35

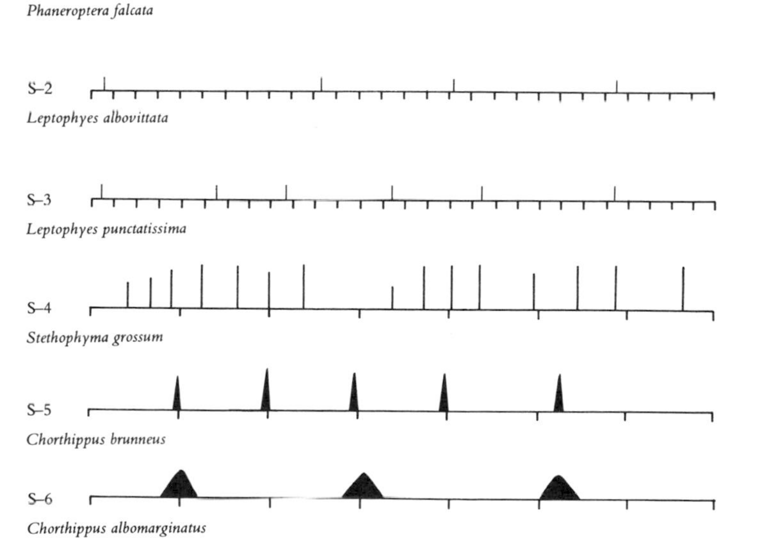

C Longer series of double sounds; intervals longer than the sounds

14. Loud double sounds with one sharp and one more prolonged component ('tzi-shipp'), often grouped in pairs (S–7). *Ephippiger ephippiger, p. 112*

D Longer series of clearly separated, sometimes differing sounds; intervals as long as or shorter than the sounds (sometimes longer for short periods)

15. Very soft double sounds with a longer, softer and a shorter, harder component ('s-ts') (S–8). *Isophya pyrenea, p. 74*

16. Quiet, soft sounds ('tsli') in quick succession (S–9). *Conocephalus discolor, p. 88*

17. Loud, sharp sounds ('tsick') in initially slower, then much quicker succession (S–10). *Decticus verrucivorus, p. 96*

18. Short scraping sounds ('tre') in uniformly quick succession, increasing somewhat in loudness (S–11). *Chorthippus vagans, p. 188*

19. Short, harshly scraping, loud sounds ('tre') in quick succession, superimposed on a continuous, softer buzzing (S–12). *Gomphocerus sibiricus, p. 176*

20. Series of buzzing sounds, increasing in loudness ('rrr-rrr-rrr') (S–13). *Myrmeleotettix maculatus, p. 180*

21. Series of impact ('ts') and buzzing ('rrr') sounds, increasing in loudness. The impact sounds predominate at the beginning of the series and the buzzing sounds towards the end (S–14). *Chorthippus mollis, p. 194*

22. Series with an alternation of buzzing and rattling sounds ('dsh-trr') (S–15). *Stauroderus scalaris, p. 182*

23. Series with one impact sound ('k') to every two buzzing sounds ('chichi') in a dense sequence, increasing in loudness at the beginning (S–16). *Chorthippus apricarius, p. 184*

E Short groups (0.5 to 5 sec.) of clearly separated, uniform sounds, with intervals between the groups

24. Very soft sounds ('tsp') arranged rhythmically in short groups (S–17). *Barbitistes serricauda, p. 76*

25. Very loud, sharp sounds ('shi') in short groups (S–18). *Pholidoptera aptera, p. 108*

26. Short scraping sounds ('zre') in quick succession in groups lasting at least 1 sec. (S–19). *Chorthippus parallelus, p. 200*

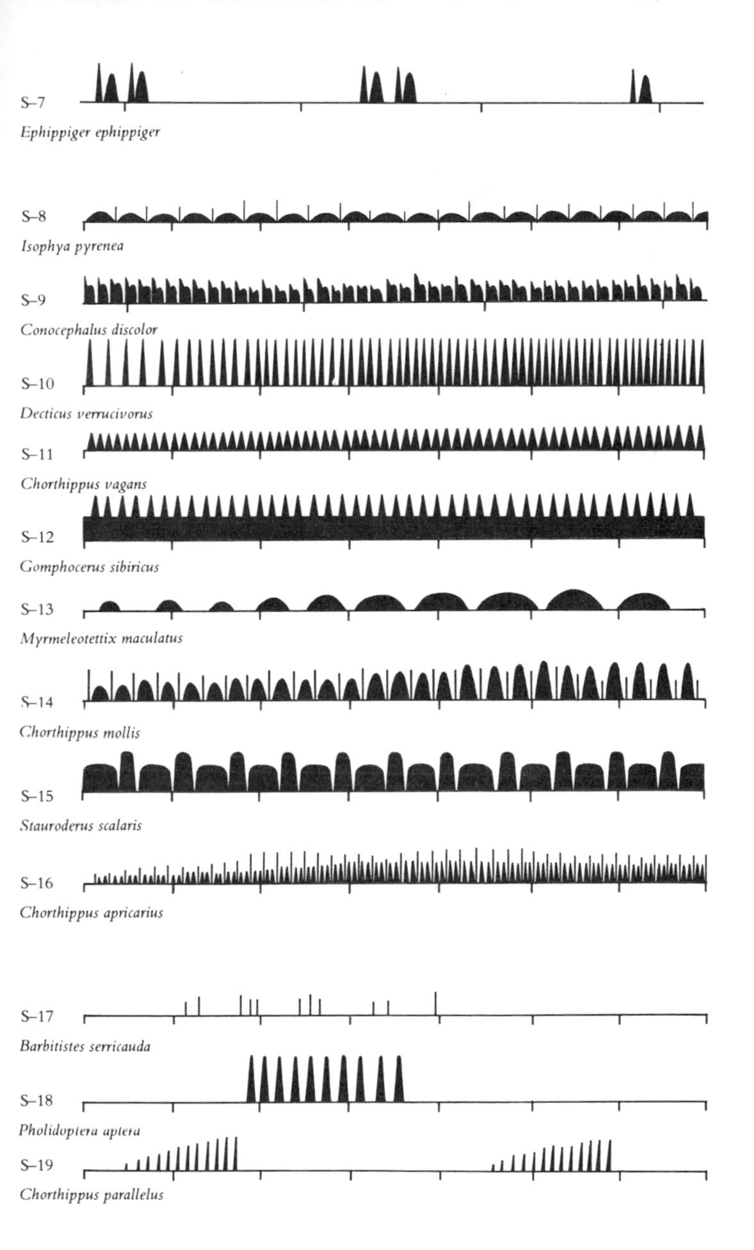
S–7
Ephippiger ephippiger
S–8
Isophya pyrenea
S–9
Conocephalus discolor
S–10
Decticus verrucivorus
S–11
Chorthippus vagans
S–12
Gomphocerus sibiricus
S–13
Myrmeleotettix maculatus
S–14
Chorthippus mollis
S–15
Stauroderus scalaris
S–16
Chorthippus apricarius
S–17
Barbitistes serricauda
S–18
Pholidoptera aptera
S–19
Chorthippus parallelus

27. Similar to 26, but somewhat louder, less harsh and with longer intervals between the sounds (S–20). *Chorthippus montanus, p. 202*

28. Short, soft sounds ('zi') in quick succession in groups lasting no more than 1 sec. (S–21). *Chrysochraon dispar, p. 160*

29. Very short, soft sounds ('chi') in groups lasting 1–3 sec. (S–22). *Stenobothrus stigmaticus, p. 168*

30. Similar to 29, but the intervals between the sounds even shorter, the syllables merging together in very warm temperatures (S–23). *Omocestus haemorrhoidalis, p. 174*

31. Sibilant-percussive sounds ('sh') in dense groups lasting 3–5 sec., increasing in loudness at the beginning (S–24). *Gomphocerippus rufus, p. 178*

32. Ringing chirps of 2–3 sec. duration, with clearly separated syllables at the beginning, merging together later ('tttttrrrt') (S–25). *Chorthippus biguttulus, p. 190*

F Very short chirps (at most 0.5 sec.) of only just separated syllables

33. Soft chirps of four syllables ('zizizizib') (S–26). *Platycleis albopunctata, p. 100*

34. Similar to 33, but chirps of only three syllables ('tsrit') and in quicker succession (S–27). *Metrioptera brachyptera, p. 106*

35. Very short, sharp chirps of three syllables ('tsrit'), much louder than 34 and at longer intervals (S–28). *Pholidoptera griseoaptera, p. 110*

36. A rapid succession of loud, sonorous chirps, almost always of three syllables ('tsri') (S–29). *Gryllus campestris, p. 116*

37. Similar to 36, but slightly less loud and repeated irregularly; the chirps vary between two and four syllables (S–30). *Acheta domesticus, p. 118*

38. Chirps of about five soft syllables, which almost merge together ('zrrr') (S–31). *Chrysochraon brachypterus, p. 162*

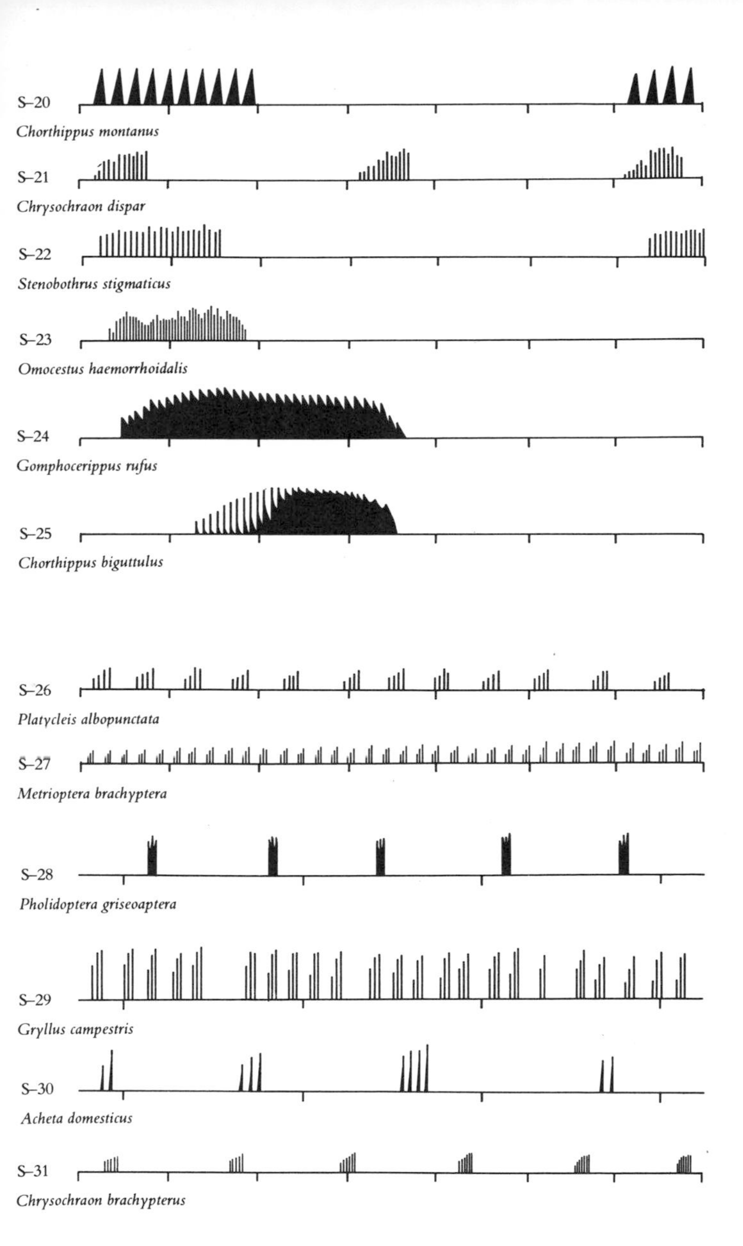
S–20
Chorthippus montanus
S–21
Chrysochraon dispar
S–22
Stenobothrus stigmaticus
S–23
Omocestus haemorrhoidalis
S–24
Gomphocerippus rufus
S–25
Chorthippus biguttulus
S–26
Platycleis albopunctata
S–27
Metrioptera brachyptera
S–28
Pholidoptera griseoaptera
S–29
Gryllus campestris
S–30
Acheta domesticus
S–31
Chrysochraon brachypterus

G Short chirps composed of separate, differing sounds

39. Short scraping sounds followed by a sizzling sound ('rerereredsh') (S–32). *Chorthippus dorsatus, p. 196*

40. Loud rasping sounds ('re') in combination with an extended buzzing sound ('tshshsh') (S–33). *Arcyptera fusca, p. 158*

41. A ringing chirp with clearly separated syllables at the beginning, merging together later. See under 32

H Short buzzing chirps

42. A soft, purring, drumming noise in short ('tr') and rather longer ('trrr') bursts (S–34). *Meconema thalassinum, p. 86*

43. Soft buzzing chirps of *c.* 1 sec. duration ('trrrrt'), separated by intervals of about equal length (S–35). *Platycleis montana, p. 102*

44. Moderately loud buzzing chirps ('tsrirrt'), increasing in duration with rising temperature, separated by short intervals (S–36). *Metrioptera bicolor, p. 106*

45. Soft buzzing chirps, gradually becoming louder, of *c.* 3 sec. duration (S–37). *Tettigonia caudata, p. 94*

46. Shrill buzzing chirps ('zirr') of *c.* 1 sec. duration, separated by intervals of about equal length (S–38). *Pteronemobius heydenii, p. 122*

47. Soft purring chirps ('rurr'), some short and some slightly longer, separated by intervals of varying length (S–39). *Nemobius sylvestris, p. 120*

48. Sharply defined, very loud, sonorous chirps of *c.* 0.5 sec. duration ('tsrruu') (S–40). *Oecanthus pellucens, p. 124*

49. Short buzzing sounds of *c.* 0.5 sec. duration at intervals of *c.* 2 sec. See under 11

50. Buzzing chirps lasting 1–2 sec. ('sssss') in an irregular sequence (S–41). *Chorthippus pullus, p. 186*

51. Buzzing chirps of *c.* 1 sec. duration, increasing in loudness and ending abruptly, usually in a sequence of three (S–42). *Stenobothrus nigromaculatus, p. 166*

52. Soft buzzing chirps of 1–3 sec. duration. See under 30

53. Synchronous ticking chirps of 3–6 sec. duration (similar to 59, but shorter) (S–43). *Omocestus rufipes, p. 172*

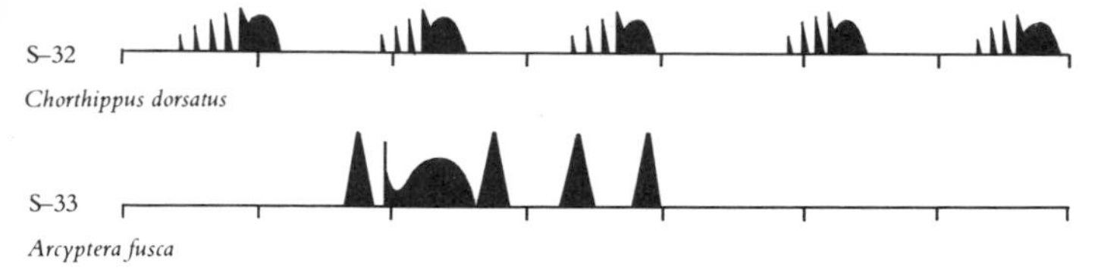
S–32
Chorthippus dorsatus
S–33
Arcyptera fusca

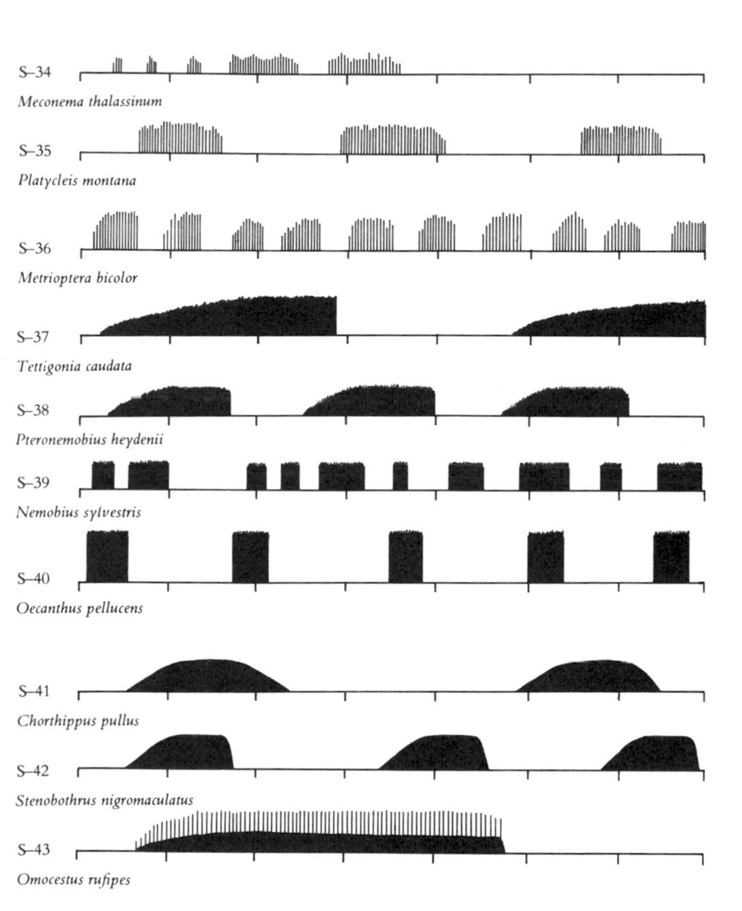
S–34
Meconema thalassinum
S–35
Platycleis montana
S–36
Metrioptera bicolor
S–37
Tettigonia caudata
S–38
Pteronemobius heydenii
S–39
Nemobius sylvestris
S–40
Oecanthus pellucens
S–41
Chorthippus pullus
S–42
Stenobothrus nigromaculatus
S–43
Omocestus rufipes

I Prolonged, uniform buzzes

54. A dull churring from the ground ('rrrrr') (S–44). *Gryllotalpa gryllotalpa, p. 124*

55. Very sharp, loud buzzes, rapidly increasing in loudness at the beginning (S–45). *Tettigonia cantans, p. 94*

56. Soft, very dense buzzes (S–46), much softer than 55. *Metrioptera roeselii, p. 104*

K Prolonged buzzes in which the syllables are distinguishable

57. Very dense, loud buzzes, into which very high-pitched squeaks are inserted at irregular intervals (S–47). *Ruspolia nitidula, p. 90*

58. Buzzes composed of clearly separate sounds: the syllables are always coupled together in pairs so that the apparent repetition rate is reduced (S–48). *Tettigonia viridissima, p. 92*

59. Soft buzzes into which ticking sounds are inserted at regular, short intervals; slowly increasing in loudness (S–49). *Omocestus viridulus, p. 170*

60. As 59, but not so prolonged. See under 53

L Prolonged buzzes with differing frequencies

61. Loud buzzes in which the frequency is high; these are followed by quite high-pitched, sharp sounds and short interruptions (S–50). For a detailed description see *p. 84*. *Polysarcus denticauda, p. 84*

62. A regular alternation of buzzing ('rrrrr') and stuttering ('ttttt') sequences (S–51). *Conocephalus dorsalis, p. 90*

63. Regularly rising and falling buzzes ('zuizuizui . . .'), rather hesitant at the beginning ('zi-zi-') (S–52). *Stenobothrus lineatus, p. 164*

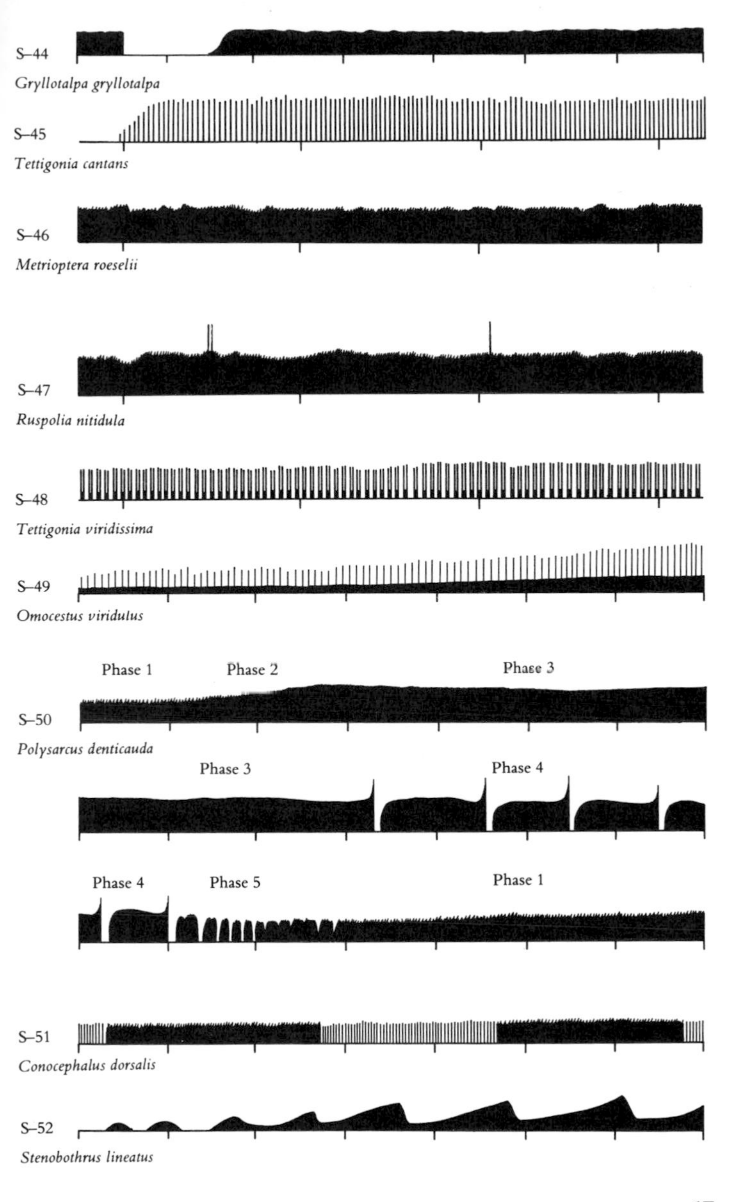
S–44
Gryllotalpa gryllotalpa
S–45
Tettigonia cantans
S–46
Metrioptera roeselii
S–47
Ruspolia nitidula
S–48
Tettigonia viridissima
S–49
Omocestus viridulus
Phase 1
Phase 2
Phase 3
S–50
Polysarcus denticauda
Phase 3
Phase 4
Phase 4
Phase 5
Phase 1
S–51
Conocephalus dorsalis
S–52
Stenobothrus lineatus

Check-list of Included Species

Suborder Ensifera (bush-crickets and crickets)

*Occurs in the British Isles (*see pp.* 35–7)

Suborder Caelifera
(ground-hoppers and grasshoppers)

FAMILY TETTIGONIIDAE (bush-crickets)

The bodies of bush-crickets are rather laterally compressed and are often coloured green. The tarsi are four-segmented. During stridulation the left fore wing is scraped over the right one. Overwintering takes place in the egg stage. The family is represented in Europe by six subfamilies.

Subfamily Phaneropterinae
Apart from *Phaneroptera* all northern European Phaneropterinae have much reduced scale-like wings. The tympanal opening is oval (*p. 10*). The ovipositor of the female is very deep and sickle-shaped, often clearly toothed at the tip, and during egg-laying is guided by the mandibles (*p. 18*, above).

Phaneroptera falcata (Sickle-bearing Bush-cricket)
Phaneroptera falcata is the only fully-winged member of the subfamily in northern Europe. The fore wings reach to near the hind knees and the hind wings are clearly longer (a condition known as 'parapterous'). The ground colour is green, sometimes tinted with rust-red on the back and legs. The whole body is speckled with fine dark spots, and ranges in length from 12 to 18mm. The antennae reach to about four times this length. The deep ovipositor is bent almost at right-angles. The male has long, strongly curved cerci. This species becomes adult in August and lives until October.

Phaneroptera falcata is very warmth-loving. It prefers to live in dry grassy undergrowth, as well as along the edges of paths and in sand-pits. It occurs widely in central Europe (including France and Germany), extending southwards to northern Spain and Portugal, northern Italy and Yugoslavia; further south it is replaced by a very similar species, *Phaneroptera nana*. Absent from Britain.

The vegetarian Sickle-bearing Bush-cricket can be kept successfully on, for example, raspberry leaves. It is very lively in the sun and if disturbed will fly long distances. The song is very quiet (audible from about 1m) and is produced particularly at dusk. The individual sounds, which can be represented roughly as 'tsb', are produced at irregular intervals. The females lay their flat eggs between the upper and lower surfaces of leaves (e.g., of sloe) (*p. 24*, above left).

Phaneroptera falcata, ♂ in flight, (Jochenstein BaW), August
Phaneroptera falcata ♀, Jockgrim Pf, August

FAMILY TETTIGONIIDAE (bush-crickets)
Subfamily Phaneropterinae

Isophya pyrenea (Large Speckled Bush-cricket)
The fore wings of the Large Speckled Bush-cricket are reduced to small lobes; the hind wings are completely absent. The ground colour is green with darker dots. A yellowish longitudinal stripe, bordered above with red-brown, runs from the eye along the side of the pronotum to the fore wing-margin. The antennae are about one and a half times the body length. The ovipositor is clearly toothed at the tip and regularly curved above and below (thus differing from the similar female of *Barbitistes*). The cerci of the male are slightly curved at the base, more strongly towards the tip, so that the ends point towards each other. The body-length varies between 16 and 26mm; the females are somewhat larger, but above all plumper than the males. This species is one of the earliest bush-crickets, adult from about the middle of June. Most adults are seen in the first half of July; some females live until the middle of September.

Isophya pyrenea lives in dry, grassy scrub, along sunny forest borders, and also in lush, rather damp meadows. The distribution extends over much of central Europe, including France, Germany and Austria, but not Britain.

The Large Speckled Bush-cricket is a pure vegetarian. It prefers to feed on soft, juicy plants like dandelion, chickweed and clover. It stays near the ground, moving very little, and is thus easily overlooked. The quiet song (audible from about 1m) is produced only in the evening and at night. It is a courtship song – a longer soft and a shorter hard sound – which can be represented as 's-ts'. This can continue for minutes without a break. During the one to two minute copulation, the male forms a particularly large spermatophore (*p. 14*, above), which the female spends many hours eating. The eggs are laid in small clusters in the ground (*p. 18*, above).

Isophya pyrenea ♂, Zimmern FrA, July
Isophya pyrenea ♀, (Schlatt SA), June

FAMILY TETTIGONIIDAE (bush-crickets)
Subfamily Phaneropterinae

Barbitistes serricauda (Saw-tailed Bush-cricket)
The Saw-tailed Bush-cricket is surely the most attractive of the western European Phaneropterinae. The ground colour is usually yellow-green, occasionally brown, with brown to black dots and spots. The dark spots can be so dense that the insect may appear generally dark, but usually the pale ground colour predominates. As in the Large Speckled Bush-cricket, a yellow line, dark-bordered below, runs from the eye along the side of the pronotum to the fore wing-margin; it may also continue on the side of the abdomen. The scale-like fore wings are rust brown in the male, green or brown in the female. The legs are often red, especially in the male. The antennae are two to three times the body-length, which amounts to *c.* 15–20mm. The red, S-shaped cerci are the most striking feature of the males. The ovipositor is almost straight below, curved upwards and clearly toothed at the tip. The insects are adult from the middle of July and live until August/September, sometimes even to October.

The habitats of this species are sunny forest borders and open heathy woodland. While the nymphs often stay on the ground, the adults are seldom found as they live on deciduous trees and bushes. However, they occasionally sun themselves on low shrubs. The distribution extends from France and Belgium eastwards across central Europe and northern Italy to northern Yugoslavia. Absent from Britain.

The Saw-tailed Bush-cricket is active mainly at dusk and in the night. It feeds almost exclusively on the leaves of woody plants, e.g., maple, hazel or raspberry. The song is produced at dusk and in the night. It is audible from about 1m and consists of 'tsp'-sounds, which are grouped together into a series of one to four. Three to five such series in turn form a phrase which has a total duration of 2–3 sec. and is separated by a longer interval from the next one. Such a phrase can be represented in the following way: 'tsptsp-tsptsptsp-tsptsp-tsp'. After mating, the female lays her flat eggs in cracks in bark or rotting wood.

Barbitistes serricauda ♂, Schelklingen SA, August
Barbitistes serricauda ♀, Schelklingen SA, July

FAMILY TETTIGONIIDAE (bush-crickets)

Subfamily Phaneropterinae

Barbitistes constrictus (Eastern Saw-tailed Bush-cricket)

The Eastern Saw-tailed Bush-cricket is very similar to the foregoing species. Its ground colour is more blue-green (but also sometimes brown) with black spots. The pronotum and top of the abdomen are often entirely black (especially in the male). In this species, a yellow longitudinal stripe also stretches backwards from the eyes. The antennae are brown to black with pale rings at long intervals. In contrast to *B. serricauda* the head is wider (somewhat wider than the length of the pronotum) and the pronotum more strongly depressed like a saddle. The S-shaped cerci of the male are broadened near the tip, then suddenly becoming narrower again (in *B. serricauda* they have the same diameter from the base to the tip). In the female the ovipositor is about two and a half to three times as long as the pronotum (in *B. serricauda* at most double the length). The size varies between 14 and 20mm; occasionally even larger individuals occur. Adulthood extends from July to October.

In contrast to the Saw-tailed Bush-cricket, this species shows a marked preference for coniferous forest. It is a mainly eastern European species, not occurring west of Germany and Austria.

So far little is known of the biology of *Barbitistes constrictus*. The only nymph I have been able to find was reared to adulthood on rose leaves as well as spruce and larch needles. The song was studied by Faber (1953). It resembles that of the Saw-tailed Bush-cricket, but has longer sequences of six to nine syllables.

Barbitistes constrictus ♂, Kellberg BaW, September, photo R. Höfels

Barbitistes constrictus ♀, (Wallenfels FrW), August

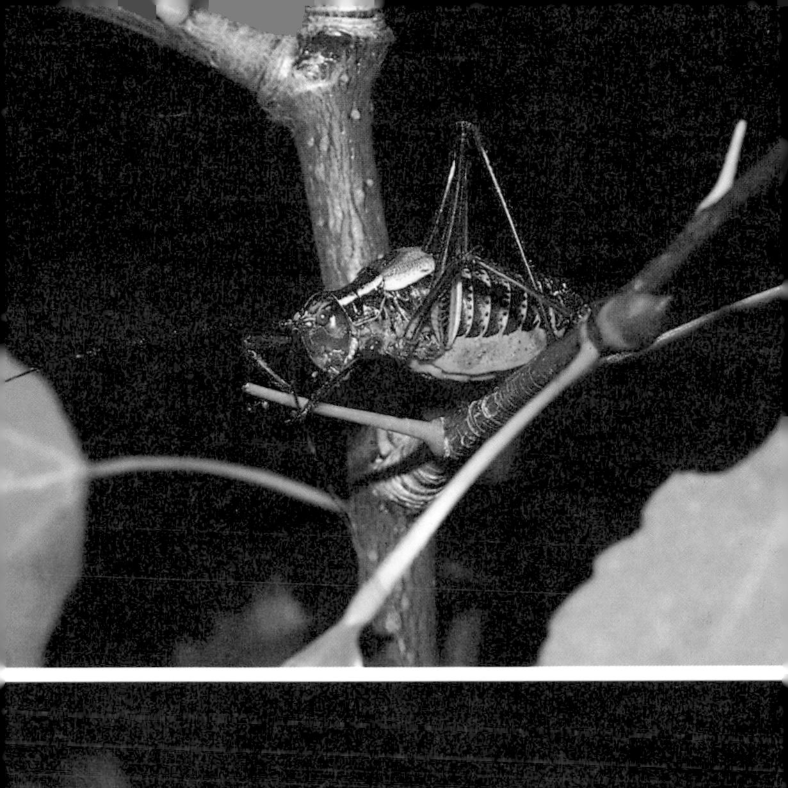

FAMILY TETTIGONIIDAE (bush-crickets)

Subfamily Phaneropterinae)

Leptophyes albovittata (Striped Bush-cricket)

The Striped Bush-cricket is only 9–14mm (♂) or 12–16mm (♀) in size. The ground colour is green with red or dark brown dots. The top of the male abdomen is usually red-brown. A longitudinal white stripe runs from the lower edge of the pronotal side-flaps along the sides of the abdomen. The saddle-shaped pronotum covers the basal half of the stumpy fore wings. The visible part of the fore wings is about half as long as the pronotum in the male and at most a third as long in the female. The antennae reach about four times the body-length. The male has fairly straight cerci, which have an inwardly directed tooth at the tip. The deep, sickle-shaped ovipositor is hardly longer than the pronotum and very finely toothed in the apical half. The insects are adult from August to September.

Leptophyes albovittata occurs mainly in southern Europe, from France and Iberia to the Balkan Peninsula; also in parts of central Europe, including Germany and Austria. Absent from Britain. It is warmth-loving and prefers to live in sunny forest borders and in dry grassy scrub.

The Striped Bush-cricket eats only plants; it particularly likes tender, succulent species, such as chickweed, meadow vetchling or dandelion. It also shows a marked preference for strongly aromatic plants. The song is so quiet that it can be heard only from about 20cm. It consists of a series of quite soft syllables ('zb'), which follow one another at intervals of about five to ten seconds at room temperature. In this species it is relatively easy to observe copulation. One has only to separate the sexes for a day and then put them together at dusk. The male humps his back like a cat and the female soon mounts him – provided she is in a sexually receptive state. After about one minute, an almost globular spermatophore flows from the male genital opening. Soon after it is deposited on the abdomen of the female the pair separate. The spermatophore is consumed in *c.* 2 hours. The flat eggs are laid in crevices in bark or in plant stems.

Leptophyes albovittata ♂, Eichstätt FrA, August
Leptophyes albovittata ♀, Heroldingen NöR, August

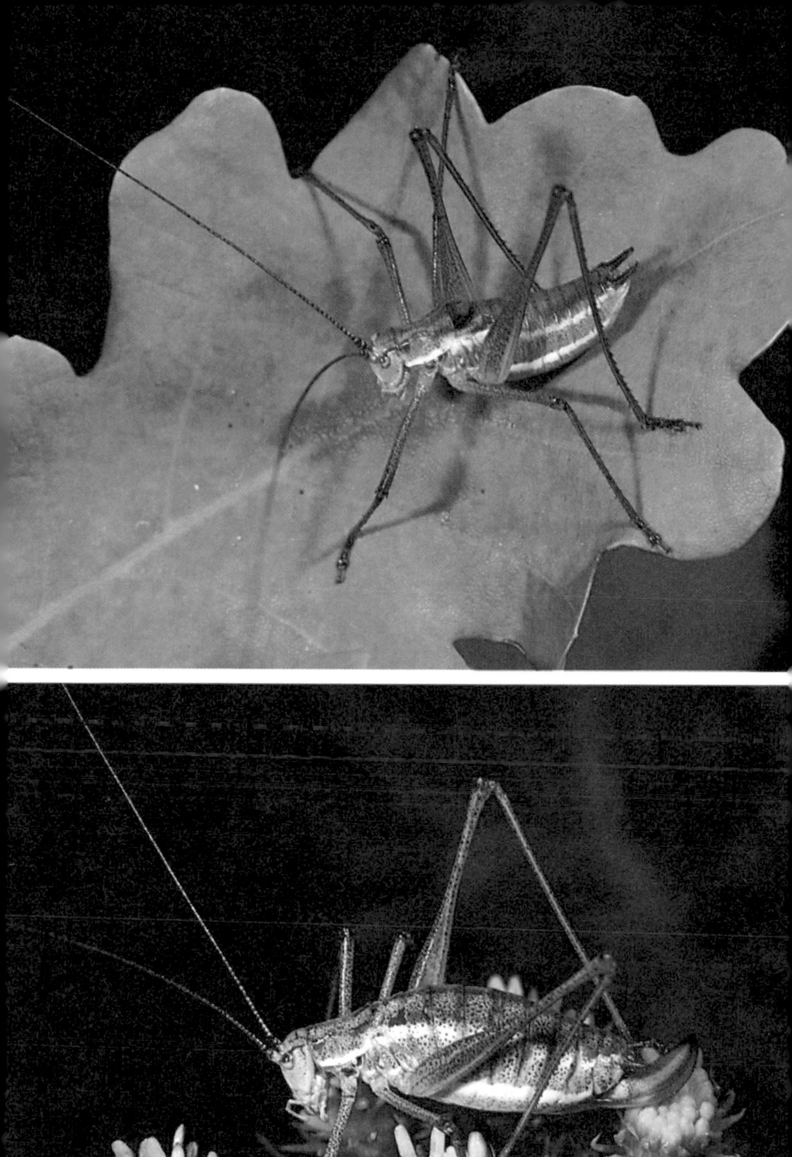

FAMILY TETTIGONIIDAE (bush-crickets)

Subfamily Phaneropterinae

Leptophyes punctatissima (Speckled Bush-cricket)
With a body-length of 10–14mm (♂) or 12–17mm (♀) the Speckled Bush-cricket is only slightly larger than the foregoing related species. Its ground colour is yellow-green with dark red speckling. A brown longitudinal stripe runs along the top of the abdomen in the male, but it is narrower than in the other species. The pronotum is shorter, the stumpy fore wings being easily visible. In the male they are rather larger than the pronotum; in the female at least half its length. The antennae again reach about four times the body-length. The cerci of the male are similar in shape to those of the Large Speckled Bush-cricket: they are almost straight in the basal part and curved inwards in the apical third. The flat, sickle-shaped ovipositor of the female is more than twice as long as the pronotum and very finely toothed in the apical third. Adulthood extends from July/August to September or October.

Leptophyes punctatissima is a follower of cultivation, liking to colonize gardens and parks. The species also particularly likes sunny forest borders. It lives mainly in undergrowth, and is not very easy to find. The Speckled Bush-cricket is very widespread in Europe, occurring from southern Scandinavia in the north to the southern peninsulas of the Mediterranean. In the British Isles it occurs in central and southern England, Wales, in the extreme south of Scotland and, patchily, in Ireland.

The species feeds almost entirely on plants: rose and raspberry leaves are as readily eaten as clover or dandelion. The song, produced in the evening and at night, is hardly louder than in *L. albovittata*; one can hear it from about 50cm. It also consists of a sequence of soft 'zb'-sounds. The intervals between the syllables are, however, somewhat shorter (about 3–6 sec. at room temperature). Mating is also relatively easy to observe in this species. It lasts somewhat longer (*c.* 5 min) and is repeated by both sexes up to eight times. Egg-laying follows in the bark of trees.

Leptophyes punctatissima ♂, (Whylen Bd), August
Leptophyes punctatissima ♀, (Whylen Bd), August

FAMILY TETTIGONIIDAE (bush-crickets)

Subfamily Phaneropterinae

Polysarcus denticauda (Large Sword-tailed Bush-cricket)

(= *Orphania denticauda*)

With a body-length of 24–44mm, this is the largest of the western European Phaneropterinae. The ground colour of its stout body is green, occasionally dark brown. The pronotum is saddle-shaped in the male, forming a resonating chamber. The stumpy fore wings of the male are yellow, usually speckled with green, and project visibly from under the pronotum; in the female they are almost completely hidden under it. Conspicuous in the male is the long, two-pronged subgenital plate, which projects upwards for some distance between the cerci. The ovipositor is long and clearly toothed at the tip. *Polysarcus* is adult as early as the beginning of June and is already dying out in the middle of July.

The Large Sword-tailed Bush-cricket occurs widely in central Europe (including south-west Germany), extending westwards to the French uplands (including the north side of the Pyrenees) and southwards to the Apennines; it is absent from Britain. Its typical habitat is meadows with long grass and luxuriant vegetation.

This sluggish species is vegetarian. If danger threatens it remains motionless, but betrays itself by its loud song, audible from about 30–50m. The song is composed of five phases. Phase 1 consists of a long, uniform sequence of buzzing sounds, during parts of which the bush-cricket wanders about. In Phase 2 the frequency is distinctly higher and the insect stands still. Phase 3 is a uniform, very shrill buzz which usually lasts *c.* 10 sec. Phase 4 is characterized by a series of five to nine quite sharp 'tsick'-sounds, which follow one another at ever-decreasing intervals. In Phase 5, a succession of 'stuttering' syllables follows, leading back to Phase 1.

Sometimes this bush-cricket occurs in unusually large numbers. It then forms a special migratory phase, like the locusts, clearly distinguished from the normal form by darker colouring, smaller size and more strongly saddle-shaped pronotum.

Polysarcus denticauda ♂, Schlatt SA, July
Polysarcus denticauda ♀, Schlatt SA, July

FAMILY TETTIGONIIDAE (bush-crickets)

Subfamily Meconematinae

The Meconematinae are small, arboreal bush-crickets with oval tympana but lacking stridulatory organs. Only two species occur in northern and central Europe.

Meconema thalassinum (Oak Bush-cricket)
(= *M. varium*)
This pale green species reaches 12–15mm in body-length. At the back of the pronotum there are two brown flecks in a yellow longitudinal stripe. The wings extend beyond the abdomen. The antennae reach about four times the body-length. In the male the cerci are slender, long (3mm), pincer-like and gently incurved. The 9mm ovipositor is sword-shaped. The species is adult from the end of July. Females sometimes survive until November.

The Oak Bush-cricket lives only in trees (especially oaks) and is therefore difficult to find (although it often occurs in gardens and parks). It occurs widely in Europe, from southern Sweden in the north to the northern parts of Spain, Italy and the Balkan Peninsula in the south. It is quite common in southern Britain and recorded from Limerick in Ireland.

This bush-cricket is nocturnal and rests during the day on the underside of leaves. After dark it hunts for small insects, e.g., caterpillars and greenflies. It is entirely predaceous and thus very beneficial. Although the males have no stridulatory organ, they produce a very characteristic song: they drum with a hind leg on the substrate (e.g., a leaf), producing a purring sound audible from about 1m. Usually there are several such bursts of drumming in a series of short bursts followed by one to three longer ones, e.g., 'tr-tr-tr-trrr-trrr'. The female lays her eggs in crevices and cracks in bark.

Meconema meridionale (Southern Oak Bush-cricket)
(= *M. brevipenne*)
The Southern Oak Bush-cricket is distinguished from *M. thalassinum* by thick, shortened, stumpy wings, and shorter ovipositor (7.5mm); the cerci of the male are longer (4mm).

This species occurs in southern France, south-west Germany, Switzerland, Austria, Italy and Yugoslavia, but not Britain. Hardly anything is known of its biology.

Meconema thalassinum ♀, (Ulm SA), September
Meconema meridionale ♂, Divaca Sl, September

FAMILY TETTIGONIIDAE (bush-crickets)

Subfamily Conocephalinae (cone-heads)

In the cone-heads the tympanal opening is closed except for a narrow slit. The head extends forwards and upwards to a point. In central and northern Europe there are three hygrophilous species.

Conocephalus discolor (Long-winged Cone-head)

(= *C. fuscus*, *Xiphidium fuscum*)

The Long-winged Cone-head reaches 12–17mm in body-length. The colour is pale green with a brown, pale-bordered, longitudinal stripe along the back. The antennae reach about three times the body-length. The noticeably narrow fore wings extend slightly beyond the hind knees. The almost straight ovipositor is nearly as long as the body. In the male the cerci have an inwardly directed tooth near the tip. The species is adult from the end of July. It lives until October, but nymphs can often still be found in September.

Conocephalus discolor occurs widely in Europe, from northern Germany to the Mediterranean coast. In Britain it occurs near the south coast of England, from Dorset to Kent, including the Isle of Wight. The species lives in marshes, reed-beds and near water. It also occurs occasionally on wasteland.

The food consists of grasses and other plants, as well as small insects such as greenflies and caterpillars. The song is audible from about 2m. It consists of a uniform series of closely spaced sounds, which can be represented as 'tslitslitsli . . .'; there are about ten syllables per second and the series often continues for long periods without interruption. The female lays the small, whitish eggs singly in the leaf-sheaths of sedges (*p. 18*, below). Sometimes she first bites a hole, through which she guides the ovipositor. The nymphs of this and the following species have, in addition to the pointed head typical of the subfamily, a sharply-defined, black longitudinal stripe along the back (*p. 25*, above right).

Conocephalus discolor ♀, Baustetten OS, August

FAMILY TETTIGONIIDAE (bush-crickets)

Subfamily Conocephalinae (cone-heads)

Conocephalus dorsalis (Short-winged Cone-head)

(= *Xiphidium dorsale*)

The Short-winged Cone-head is similar to *C. discolor* in size (11–18mm) and colouring. However, the wings are greatly shortened, not reaching the end of the abdomen. Very occasionally, a long-winged form occurs. The female of this form is distinguished from *C. discolor* by the shorter, clearly curved ovipositor, and the male by the longer lateral tooth of the cerci. The species is adult from July to October.

The Short-winged Cone-head is widespread in Europe, extending its range well into Scandinavia in the north, but not reaching the extreme south. It occurs patchily in southern Britain, especially in coastal counties. It lives in damp places.

The song is softer than in the Long-winged Cone-head, and is composed of two quite different, regularly alternating sounds. A uniform buzzing alternates from time to time with a distinctly deeper, rather stuttering song: 'rrrrr-ttttt-rrrrr-tttttt . . .'.

Ruspolia nitidula (Large Cone-head)

(= *Homorocoryphus nitidulus*, *Conocephalus mandibularis*)

With a body-length of 20–29mm, *Ruspolia nitidula* is clearly larger than the other cone-heads. It is almost uniformly pale green, occasionally brownish or reddish. The antennae are slightly shorter than the body. The straight ovipositor is almost as long as the body. The male cerci have two small incurved teeth at the tip. Adults are found from August to October.

This species occurs in moist meadows and wasteland (and sometimes dry fields of long grass) throughout southern Europe, including most of France and southern Germany. Absent from Britain.

The song is a very high-pitched loud buzzing, into which quite sharp, almost ultrasonic, 'squeaking' sounds are inserted at regular intervals.

Conocephalus dorsalis ♀, Neuenkirchen LH, August
Ruspolia nitidula ♀, Limski Canal Is, September

FAMILY TETTIGONIIDAE (bush-crickets)

Subfamily Tettigoniinae

The Tettigoniinae have slit-like tympanal openings. They are large, robust insects with green ground colouring. The fore wings are uniformly green, or brown along the back, but never with square dark spots. The antennae reach about one and a half times the body-length in all three species.

Tettigonia viridissima (Great Green Bush-cricket)
With a body-length of 28–36mm (♂) or 32–42mm (♀), this species is the largest bush-cricket in northern Europe. This otherwise green insect is usually coloured brown along the back. Occasionally, as in the illustration, the legs are yellow. Rarely all-yellow individuals occur. The ovipositor reaches nearly to the tips of the very long wings (the species is an active flier). In the male the cerci, which are toothed near the base, are clearly longer than the styles. *Tettigonia viridissima* is adult from the middle of July and sometimes survives until the end of October.

This species is one of the most adaptable bush-crickets. It lives on cultivated land, including gardens and cornfields, as well as sunny waysides and dry fields. It is very widespread in Europe and often abundant, but avoids higher altitudes, where it is replaced by the following species (*T. cantans*). It occurs patchily in southern Britain, especially near the coast and in the West Country. The food consists largely of insects: flies, caterpillars, even beetle larvae, are readily eaten. Vegetable food seems to serve only as a supplementary diet. The Great Green Bush-cricket is thus a very useful garden inhabitant – a little-known fact, unfortunately! The species is active by day and night, singing from about midday to midnight. The song is a loud buzzing audible from about 50m. As two syllables are coupled into a double sound, the song – in contrast to *T. cantans* – is always clearly cut up into 'pulses' of sound. After mating, the female lays the dark brown slender eggs singly or in small groups in the ground. The embryonic development lasts at least a year and a half, sometimes even up to five years.

Tettigonia viridissima ♂, Baustetten OS, September

FAMILY TETTIGONIIDAE (bush-crickets)

Subfamily Tettigoniinae

Tettigonia cantans (Upland Green Bush-cricket)

With a body-length of 20–30mm (♂) or 25–33mm (♀), the Upland Green Bush-cricket is on average smaller than the Great Green Bush-cricket. As the wings are clearly shortened (reaching about as far as the hind knees) this flightless species appears even smaller. The ovipositor extends beyond the wings by about 15mm. The adult life-span extends from the end of July until October.

The Upland Green Bush-cricket prefers damp places, especially meadows. Occasionally it occurs together with *T. viridissima*, but usually the occurrence of the two species is mutually exclusive. It is most abundant in high uplands (where *T. viridissima* is usually absent), occurring widely in the mountains of central and southern Europe, including the Pyrenees, Vosges, Jura, Alps and Apennines, but is very local in northern Europe. Absent from Britain.

Tettigonia cantans seems to prefer plant to animal food. Its song is an even, very loud buzzing, so that individual syllables cannot be distinguished. The rate of wing-vibration is similar to that of *T. viridissima*, but the individual syllables are equally spaced, so that the song seems to be a uniform buzz. Only in very cool weather is the rate of wing-vibration slow enough for the individual syllables to be clearly audible.

Tettigonia caudata (Eastern Green Bush-cricket)

Tettigonia caudata is intermediate in body-size and wing-length between *T. viridissima* and *T. cantans*. The ovipositor extends beyond the wing-tips by about 10mm. In the male the cerci and styles are about the same length. The conspicuous, black-bordered spines on the underside of the hind femora provide a reliable diagnostic character. The Eastern Green Bush-cricket occurs in eastern Europe, from East Germany and Austria eastwards. It prefers to live in cornfields and wasteland along roadsides.

The song consists of short bursts of buzzing, each of which begins quietly and becomes louder. It sounds distinctly softer than *T. cantans* and is audible only from about 10–20m.

Tettigonia cantans ♀, Wurzach OS, August
Tettigonia caudata ♀, Baderna Is, July

FAMILY TETTIGONIIDAE (bush-crickets)

Subfamily Decticinae

The Decticinae have slit-like tympanal openings and – as a hallmark – movable paired flaps on the first segment of the hind tarsi. The fore wings are often marked with square spots; in many species they are greatly shortened.

Decticus verrucivorus (Wart-biter)

The Wart-biter reaches 24–38mm (♂) or 26–44mm (♀) in body-length, about the same size as the Great Green Bush-cricket. Because of its shorter wings, which do not usually reach the hind knees, it appears smaller. The antennae are about as long as the body. The colour is very variable; it can vary between green, yellow-brown and blackish brown, and is usually mottled with various colours. The fore wings are usually marked with square spots. The long ovipositor is slightly curved. The cerci of the males are toothed shortly beyond the middle.

The Wart-biter is a typical ground-dweller, occurring most abundantly on the short grass of alpine meadows. It also occurs in damp meadows and dry fields. It is widespread in Europe, including Scandinavia, but is absent from parts of the south. It is very local in southern England, where it is always green in colour.

The Wart-biter feeds mostly on insects, but also on plants. It is markedly diurnal and sings only in sunshine. The song is a sequence of 'tick'-sounds. These are at first hesitant, then follow each other ever more closely, but the individual syllables always remain clearly audible. In copulation the male stands on its head and firmly grasps the ovipositor of the upright-standing female with its fore legs. The female later lays her pale eggs singly in the ground. The embryonic development lasts at least one and a half years. The name Wart-biter comes from ancient folk-lore: people used to allow Wart-biters to bite off their warts, 'cauterizing' them with the secretion produced. This remedy was supposed to be very effective.

Decticus verrucivorus ♂, Pfullingen SA, August
Decticus verrucivorus ♀, Pfullingen SA, August

FAMILY TETTIGONIIDAE (bush-crickets)

Subfamily Decticinae

Gampsocleis glabra (Heath Bush-cricket)

The Heath Bush-cricket looks rather similar to the Wart-biter, but is smaller and more graceful. Both sexes reach 20–26mm in body-length. The colouring is mostly green with brown markings on the fore wings. The ovipositor is slightly downcurved and obliquely truncate at the tip. The cerci of the male are triangular and flattened, with a tooth near the base. The species is adult from the beginning of July to September.

The Heath Bush-cricket lives in dry, steppe-like regions with high grass (e.g., *Stipa* spp.) or heather. It is very sensitive to changes in its habitat. It occurs from the Low Countries and France in the west, across central to eastern Europe, and southwards to northern Spain and northern Yugoslavia. Absent from Britain.

Gampsocleis glabra is very dependent on warmth and active only in sunshine. The song is a loud buzzing and can be compared with that of *Tettigonia viridissima* or *Metrioptera roeselii*, as well as that of the bird, the Grasshopper Warbler.

Gampsocleis glabra, ♂ singing, Bugac/Hungary, August, Photo Dr S. Ingrisch

FAMILY TETTIGONIIDAE (bush-crickets)
Subfamily Decticinae

Platycleis albopunctata (Grey Bush-cricket)
(= *P. denticulata*, *Metrioptera grisea* part)
The Grey Bush-cricket is 18–22mm long and is almost always brown in colour, with the fore wings dark brown with whitish spots. The top of the head and pronotum is usually paler (e.g., often red-brown). Very rarely this insect is partly green. The ovipositor is about 10mm long and clearly curved. The cerci of the male are toothed near the tip. Adult insects occur from the end of June to September.

Platycleis albopunctata is very warmth-loving. It lives in dry places with sparse vegetation, especially south-facing stony slopes. It is widespread in western Europe, from Scandinavia to the Iberian Peninsula and including Germany and Switzerland. In Britain it is found only in southern England and Wales, especially near the coast. The Grey Bush-cricket is diurnal and flies readily in warm conditions. The song consists of a soft chirping, usually in groups of four syllables that merge together in warm temperatures into short chirps lasting *c.* 0.2 sec. The chirps follow one another in rapid succession, sounding rather like 'zizizizib'.

In southern Europe the extremely similar *Platycleis grisea* occurs, which can be distinguished from *P. albopunctata* only by genital morphology. Both species were formerly treated as the single species *P. grisea* or *Metrioptera grisea*.

Platycleis albopunctata ♂,
Hirschau near Tübingen, September
Platycleis albopunctata ♀,
Hirschau near Tübingen, September

FAMILY TETTIGONIIDAE (bush-crickets)

Subfamily Decticinae

Platycleis montana (Steppe Bush-cricket)

The Steppe Bush-cricket is rather similar to the Grey Bush-cricket, but is clearly smaller (14–18mm). In addition to brown specimens there is a form in which the top of the head, the pronotum and the hind femur are coloured green. The wings fall well short of the hind knees. The ovipositor is somewhat longer than in *P. albopunctata* (10–12mm). The cerci of the male have a backwardly-curved tooth near the base. Adults occur from July to October.

This species lives in dry habitats (fallow land, steppe). It is primarily eastern European, but occurs in Austria and, very locally, in Germany. Absent from Britain.

The song consists of chirps sounding rather like 'trrrrt' and lasting at least 1 sec. They are separated by pauses of about the same length.

Platycleis tessellata (Brown-spotted Bush-cricket)

With a body-length of only 14–16mm, the Brown-spotted Bush-cricket is the smallest northern European Decticine. The ground colour is yellow-brown to brown. Along the middle of the almost sickle-shaped fore wings runs a dark brown longitudinal band which is interrupted by narrow pale oblique stripes (partly hidden by the hind femur in the illustration). The ovipositor is very short (*c.* 5mm) and curved like a sickle. The adults live from July to September.

This southern European species is very dependent on warmth. It is widespread in France, the Iberian Peninsula, Italy and Yugoslavia, occurs very rarely in Germany and is absent from Britain. Its habitat is dry, almost barren waste places.

The song is known to me only from a record (Grein 1984). It consists of scratchy chirps of *c.* 0.2 sec. duration, sounding rather like 'rebb' and separated by intervals of *c.* 1 sec.

Platycleis montana ♂, Podersdorf Bu, July
Platycleis tessellata ♂, Pula Is, July

FAMILY TETTIGONIIDAE (bush-crickets)
Subfamily Decticinae

Metrioptera roeselii (Roesel's Bush-cricket)
Roesel's Bush-cricket is named after Roesel von Rosenhof, who, with his famous *Insectenbelustigungen*, became one of the pioneers of scientific nature study about 200 years ago. Roesel's detailed, excellently illustrated observation of the mating behaviour of the Wart-biter dates, for example, from that time. The bush-cricket named after him reaches 14–18mm in body-length. The ground colour is green or pale brown. The darker side-flaps of the pronotum are broadly margined with yellow-white or pale green. The brownish, sometimes green-striped fore wings cover about half the abdomen; fully-winged insects also occur occasionally (*p. 38*, above). In the length of the ovipositor (7–8mm), *M. roeselii* is intermediate between the other two *Metrioptera* species. The cerci of the male are toothed in the apical third. The species is adult from the beginning of July to October.

Metrioptera roeselii is the most common bush-cricket in much of Europe, occurring in damp and dry grassland from southern Scandinavia to Spain. Local in Britain, usually near estuaries, and recorded from one locality in Ireland.

Metrioptera roeselii feeds predominantly on grasses; occasionally it also eats small insects. It is mainly diurnal, the song being heard after dark only on warm nights. The song is a soft, high-pitched, completely uniform buzz, which is only briefly interrupted at long intervals. In comparison with the harsh buzz of *Tettigonia cantans*, the *M. roeselii* song is distinctly softer and quieter, audible from only about 10m; nevertheless a whole meadow can be filled with its song. When laying eggs the female usually bites a hole in a plant stem (e.g., thistle) and guides the ovipositor through it. The eggs are laid singly or in small groups.

Metrioptera roeselii ♂, Allmendingen SA, August
Metrioptera roeselii ♀, Gerhausen SA, July

FAMILY TETTIGONIIDAE (bush-crickets)

Subfamily Decticinae

Metrioptera brachyptera (Bog Bush-cricket)

In its body-length of 12–18mm, the Bog Bush-cricket is roughly the same size as *M. roeselii*. Its ground colour is dark brown, often nearly black, usually with green on the top of the pronotum and with partly green fore wings. Long-winged insects are only very occasionally found among the normal short-winged ones. There is a very narrow pale band on only the hind margin of the pronotal side-flaps. The 8–10mm ovipositor is longer than in *M. roeselii*; the cerci of the male are toothed shortly before the middle. The species is adult from July to October.

Metrioptera brachyptera is more restricted to damp meadows than *M. roeselii*; however, but can occur in dry meadows with long grass. In general, it is less common than *M. roeselii*, but occurs continuously over wide areas. It is widely distributed in Europe, from Lapland in the north to the Pyrenees, northern Italy and Yugoslavia in the south. In the British Isles it usually occurs on damp heathland and is confined to England and the extreme south of Scotland. The song closely resembles that of *Platycleis albopunctata*. There are usually three syllables grouped together into a short chirp ('tsrit'), produced in long sequences, audible from *c.* 2m.

Metrioptera bicolor (Two-coloured Bush-cricket)

It is about the same size as the other species of the genus (15–18mm). It is usually pale green with brown on the top of the pronotum, occasionally uniformly yellow-brown. Besides the normal, short-winged specimens one can find a long-winged form. The 5–6mm ovipositor is shorter than in the other *Metrioptera* species. The cerci of the male are toothed near the tip. Adult insects are found from July to September. *M. bicolor* is warmth-loving and occurs only in dry meadows. Distribution similar to *M. brachyptera*, but does not occur as far north in Scandinavia; absent from Britain.

In low temperatures, one can clearly detect the individual syllables of the song; when it is warmer they merge into a uniform 'tsrirrt', which at even higher temperatures is extended to minutes in duration, only briefly interrupted.

Metrioptera brachyptera ♂, Baustetten OS, August
Metrioptera bicolor ♀, Allmendingen SA, August

FAMILY TETTIGONIIDAE (bush-crickets)
Subfamily Decticinae

Pholidoptera aptera (Alpine Dark Bush-cricket)
(= *Thamnotrizon apterus*)

The Alpine Dark Bush-cricket is 19–22mm (♂) or 22–25mm (♀) in size. The ground colour is red-brown to grey-brown. In a brightly-coloured male, the sides of the pronotum are black, the 6–8mm fore wings yellow-brown. The underside is bright pale yellow. The females are more uniformly coloured; their fore wings are no more than 2mm long and protrude only slightly from under the pronotum. Both sexes have a sharply-defined, yellow-white band on the hind margin of the pronotal side-flaps. The ovipositor is almost as long as the body and slightly curved. The long, almost straight cerci of the male are toothed near the base. The species is adult from the beginning of July to October.

The distribution of the Alpine Dark Bush-cricket extends from the Cevennes in France across the Alps to northern Italy and the uplands of central and eastern Europe; it is absent from Britain. It prefers to live in forest glades in montane regions. Dense populations often occur in clearings with copious growths of bracken and brambles. It is, however, very difficult to catch such an unusually active insect.

The song is very loud and conspicuous, audible from about 50m. It consists of a short sequence of sharp, rapidly repeated chirps and sounds rather like 'shishishishishi'. There is often a regular alternation song between two males, in which the 'shi' sound of one of them always falls exactly in the pause between two chirps of the other.

Pholidoptera aptera ♂, Laax Gr, August
Pholidoptera aptera ♀, Laax Gr, August

FAMILY TETTIGONIIDAE (bush-crickets)

Subfamily Decticinae

Pholidoptera griseoaptera (Dark Bush-cricket)

(= *Thamnotrizon cinereus*)

The Dark Bush-cricket reaches a body-length of 13–15mm (♂) or 15–18mm (♀) and is clearly smaller than its alpine sister species. The ground colour in this species also varies between grey-brown and red-brown; yellow-brown insects also occur. The underside is a very striking bright yellow. The pronotal side-flaps are very narrowly pale-bordered behind. The fore wings are up to 5mm long in the male, only about 1mm in the female. The strongly curved ovipositor is 9–10mm long. In the male, the long straight cerci – as in *Ph. aptera* – are toothed at the base. The species is adult from the middle or end of July to October/November.

Pholidoptera griseoaptera prefers to live in forest glades and along forest borders, as well as in dry, grassy scrub and wasteland. It is very widely distributed in Europe, from Lapland to northern Spain, northern Italy and Yugoslavia. In the British Isles it is common in southern England, local in Wales, especially on the coast, and in the north reaches the extreme south of Scotland; it also occurs on the Isle of Man and, rarely, in Ireland.

The Dark Bush-cricket eats insects – caterpillars, flies, greenflies, etc. – as well as plants, e.g., dandelion, stinging nettles. The easily-recognized nymphs (which are brown with a yellow stripe, edged with blackish-brown along the back) are plentiful in May/June along forest borders, and can be reared to adulthood on purely vegetable food. The adults are active by day and night. The characteristic shrill song of the male can be heard through the day and into the night. It usually consists of three syllables ('tsitsitsi'), which at higher temperatures merge completely into a sharp 'tsrit', audible from about 10m. As a reaction to disturbance by another male, more of these syllables are added together to form a louder sequence. The song can often be heard along forest tracks even in misty, overcast weather and even after the first night frost, but it is not usually easy to find the songsters.

Pholidoptera griseoaptera ♂, Wiblingen OS, August
Pholidoptera griseoaptera ♀, Wiblingen OS, August

FAMILY TETTIGONIIDAE (bush-crickets)
Subfamily Ephippigerinae

The Ephippigerinae are characterized by the shape of their pronotum: it is horizontal in the front part (prozona) and is then suddenly raised up like a funnel in the hind part (metazona), so that there is usually a distinct angle between the pro- and metazona. The fore wings are greatly reduced and lie like rounded scales, partly hidden under the pronotum. Tympanal openings are slit-like. There are short-winged species with similar pronota in other subfamilies.

Ephippiger ephippiger (Saddle-backed Bush-cricket)
(= *E. vitium*)
The Saddle-backed Bush-cricket is the only Ephippigerine in north-west Europe. The size varies between 22 and 25mm (♂) or 24 and 30mm (♀). The ground colour is very variable, usually pale green to olive green, also sometimes yellowish or blue-green. The sharply-defined, black colour of the back of the head, revealed particularly when the head is bent forward, is very noticeable. The gently incurved ovipositor is almost as long as the body. The male has quite short, conical cerci with a small inner tooth. The species is sometimes adult in July, but usually not until August; it lives until October.

This interesting bush-cricket occurs from the Low Countries, France and northern Spain eastwards across central Europe (including south-west Germany) and northern Italy to the Balkan Peninsula; it is absent from Britain. It colonizes only the warmest places with minimal rainfall.

The Saddle-backed Bush-cricket likes a vegetable diet, such as blackberry leaves and dandelion, as much as flies and caterpillars. The vigorous, shrill chirp is to be heard during the day and night. It is composed of two sounds coupled together, one sharp and quite short, and one more prolonged following immediately. One such double-sound can be represented as 'tsi-shipp'. The female can also produce a similar sound and responds in this way to the male.

The taxonomy of this species still causes great problems. It seems possible that the insects living south of the Alps (including the female in the lower illustration) belong to a distinct species (Nadig, personal communication).

Ephippiger ephippiger ♂, Schlossböckelheim Pf, August
Ephippiger ephippiger ♀, Castaneda Gr, August

FAMILY RHAPHIDOPHORIDAE (wingless camel-crickets)

The wingless camel-crickets have neither wings nor hearing organs. The antennae, the legs, and also the maxillary and labial palps, are strongly elongated. Most species live in caves and other dark, damp places in the Mediterranean region as well as the tropics. Only one introduced species occurs in north-west Europe.

Tachycines asynamorus (Greenhouse Camel-cricket)
The Greenhouse Camel-cricket reaches 13–19mm in size. The ground colour is yellow-brown or grey-brown with dark brown mottling. The long grey-brown legs are dark-banded. The stout body is arched in side view and appears humped. The antennae reach about four times the body-length. The ovipositor is gently curved and 11–12mm long. The cerci are similar in the two sexes, about 10mm long, flexible and with erect hairs. Adult insects can be found throughout the year.

The Greenhouse Camel-cricket came originally from the Far East, probably from China, and is now distributed throughout the world. It was introduced into Europe towards the end of the last century and is now widespread in greenhouses in both continental Europe and Britain. It is not easy to know where *Tachycines* occurs as it is nocturnal. During the day it rests motionless between flowerpots, under boards and in similar places, and is active only in complete darkness. It is extremely agile and can jump more than a metre. Its food consists of fruit, seedlings and various insects, e.g., greenflies. When abundant it can be harmful. Before mating, the male courts the female by making silent rocking movements in front of her. The numerous eggs (several hundred) are most often laid in flowerpots, so that the species can easily be spread. The nymphs reach maturity only after about ten moults.

Tachycines asynamorus ♂, (Ulm Aquarium), April
Tachycines asynamorus ♀, (Ulm Aquarium), December

FAMILY GRYLLIDAE (crickets)

The body of a cricket is usually cylindrical, the colour black, blackish-brown or yellowish – never green. The tarsi are three-segmented; the tympanal opening is exposed (absent in *Myrmecophilus*). The cerci are long, flexible and hairy. Apart from *Oecanthus* the native species are ground-dwelling insects overwintering as nymphs and mature by spring. During stridulation they scrape the right fore wing over the left one.

Gryllus campestris (Field-cricket) (= *Liogryllus campestris*) The black colouring and sturdy build make the Field-cricket unmistakable. It reaches 20–26mm in body-length. The hind femora are red below. The fore wings completely conceal the vestigial hind wings; they are brownish with yellow at the base, and strikingly sculptured in the male. The stridulatory rib runs zig-zag across the fore wing, dividing it into a basal, triangular region, the 'harp', and an apical, round 'mirror' (*Fig.* 6 **A**). The harp and mirror form the sounding-board for amplifying the song. In the female, however, the fore wings are regularly veined. The ovipositor is enlarged at the tip. Adults are found from about May to July.

The Field-cricket lives in dry, sunny areas with low vegetation, e.g., dry fields and heaths. It occurs widely in Europe except for the extreme north. In Britain it is confined to one or two localities in southern England. A very similar species, *Gryllus bimaculatus*, occurs in southern Europe; it differs from *G. campestris* in having fully-developed hind wings, extending well beyond the fore wings, and thus being able to fly.

The older nymphs and adults live in burrows, leading obliquely downwards for about 20cm, which they dig themselves. They feed on grasses, various herbs and small insects. The males stridulate in warm weather from in front of the burrow entrance, often until late at night, and are audible from about 50m. The chirp sounds rather like 'tsri' and is repeated interminably in rapid succession. The males often engage in fights, accompanied by a special 'whipping' sound. In courting, the male produces special, soft sounds, audible only in the immediate vicinity. The nymphs moult in the summer and usually overwinter in the penultimate instar.

Gryllus campestris, ♂ singing in front of the burrow, Posthausen near Bremen, June

FAMILY GRYLLIDAE (crickets)

Acheta domesticus (House-cricket)

(= *Gryllulus domesticus*)

With a body-length of 16–20mm the House-cricket is somewhat smaller than the Field-cricket, and also distinctly slimmer. The ground colour is straw-yellow to yellow-brown. The pronotum and head have black markings. The hind wings are fully developed and, when flexed, extend beyond the tip of the abdomen, folded up like two spikes. The female has a straight ovipositor up to 15mm long. Adult insects occur throughout the year.

In Europe the House-cricket can maintain itself permanently only in buildings. In summer it also lives in the open, especially on refuse tips. In spite of control measures the species is still common in many places, particularly in older buildings. It occurs widely in both continental Europe and in the British Isles.

These insects are omnivorous, feeding especially on refuse but occasionally on stored food. The very loud and musical song is almost always produced in the evening or at night. It is reminiscent of the Field-cricket, but softer and less regular in the duration of the chirps and the intervals between them.

Modicogryllus frontalis (Eastern Cricket)

(= *Acheta frontalis*)

The Eastern Cricket is only about 12–13mm in size. The colour is blackish-brown with a whitish-yellow transverse band in front of the eyes. The hind wings are usually vestigial. Adulthood extends from May to the end of July.

This species occurs only in central and eastern Europe, from southern Germany (where it is perhaps now extinct) and Austria eastwards, and southwards as far as Yugoslavia. It lives in warm, dry, stony places.

According to Faber (1953) the Eastern Cricket does not have a calling song; it sings only when several crickets are together, or before and during mating.

Acheta domesticus ♂ (insect from a culture), June
Modicogryllus frontalis ♂,
specimen from Regensburg, leg. *c.* 1870

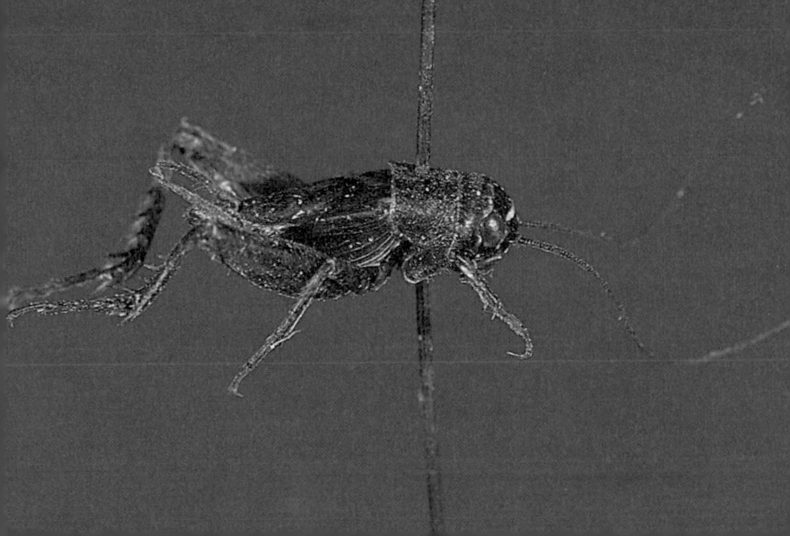

FAMILY GRYLLIDAE (crickets)

Nemobius sylvestris (Wood-cricket)

The fore wings of the Wood-cricket are shortened, reaching about halfway along the abdomen in the male, less in the female. Hind wings absent. The ground colour is dark brown; the top of the pronotum and the legs are paler. On the front of the head are four pale lines forming a forward-opening pentagon, at the base of which is an ocellus. The body-length reaches 7–10mm. The straight ovipositor is 5–7mm long. The species is adult from June and lives until late autumn (November); adults occasionally seem to over-winter in addition to eggs and nymphs. Development probably takes two years.

The Wood-cricket occurs widely in western and central Europe, from the Low Countries and Germany in the north to Spain in the south; it is very local in southern England. Its habitats are sunny forest borders and glades, as well as dry grassy scrub.

The Wood-cricket is a committed ground-dweller and particularly likes to live in leaf-litter. The insects are exceptionally agile and jump well, so that they are very difficult to catch. The song, which can be heard well into the autumn, is a very melodious, purring 'rurr', which lasts about 0.25 to 2 sec. and is repeated for minutes at a time with an occasional short interruption. The rhythm of the song is very reminiscent of Morse signals. Its direction and distance are very difficult to judge. When several insects are singing together, it is almost impossible to locate one of the singers.

Nemobius sylvestris ♂,
(Gr. Lengden near Göttingen), August

FAMILY GRYLLIDAE (crickets)

Pteronemobius heydenii (Marsh-cricket)

(= *P. concolor*)

The Marsh-cricket is reminiscent of the Wood-cricket, but is smaller (6–7mm) and almost uniformly black, with only a few whitish-yellow longitudinal lines on the back of the head, and spots on the legs. The fore wings are somewhat longer than in the Wood-cricket and the ovipositor is clearly shorter (2.5mm). Adults are found from the end of May until the beginning of August.

This species lives in marshy meadows between clumps of grass and sedge, in ditches and in wet places generally. It occurs widely in western, central and southern Europe, but not north of about 50°N latitude. Absent from Britain.

The song is shriller than in the Wood-cricket, sounding rather like 'zirr'. The individual chirps last 1–2 sec. and are separated by pauses of similar duration. Locating the Marsh-cricket by the song is also almost impossible.

Myrmecophilus acervorum (Ant-cricket)

With a body-length of no more than 3.5mm, the Ant-cricket is the smallest cricket in western Europe. The colouring is dark brown with pale hind margins on the pro- and mesonotum. The wings and hearing organs are absent, and the eyes poorly developed. The cerci, on the other hand, are well developed. The Ant-cricket often occurs only as females, which can be recognized by their short ovipositor. Adult insects are found throughout the year. Development takes two years.

The Ant-cricket lives only in ants'-nests, especially of *Lasius* species (Hölldobler 1947). These nests can be found by turning over stones. It occurs mainly in central Europe, including parts of Germany and France. Absent from Britain.

The Ant-cricket apparently lives as a parasite on ant larvae. There are two forms distinguished by size and sometimes taken to be distinct species (Harz 1969).

Pteronemobius heydenii ♂, (Taubergiessen Bd), June
Myrmecophilus acervorum ♀, (Goldburghausen NöR), September

FAMILY GRYLLIDAE (crickets)

Oecanthus pellucens (Tree-cricket)
The Tree-cricket differs greatly from the other crickets in its slender build. The ground colour is yellowish to pale brown; the body-length is 9–15mm. In the female, the straight, backwardly-directed cerci are almost as long as the ovipositor. Adults occur from August to October.

This species is very dependent on warmth. It is widespread in central and especially southern Europe (including southern France and south-west Germany), but absent from Britain. It lives mainly in dry grassy scrub, and is often found on tall flowering plants. The melodious song is a very loud 'tsrruu', audible from about 50m and produced mainly after dark. The eggs are laid above ground in plant-stems.

FAMILY GRYLLOTALPIDAE (mole-crickets)

The mole-crickets are easily recognized by their strongly-built digging limbs (the modified fore legs). They are unable to jump. The antennae are only half as long as the pronotum; the ovipositor is absent.

Gryllotalpa gryllotalpa (Mole-cricket) (= *G. vulgaris*)
The only north European species is unmistakable from the characters given above. The ground colour is dark brown. The body-length can reach 50mm. The sexes are difficult to distinguish, but in the male the veins in about the middle of the fore wing branch like a forwardly-opening tuning-fork. Adults are found over the year; development takes 3 years.

The Mole-cricket lives mainly in damp, loose soil with low grass, but also in loamy soil. It feeds predominantly on animal food, especially insect larvae. During stridulation either of the two fore wings can lie above the other. The song is a long, continuous churring ('rrrrr'), which is mostly produced in the evenings in May/June. The female guards the eggs and young nymphs in a special nest-chamber.

This species occurs widely in northern, western and central Europe, including France and Germany and reaching as far north as southern Scandinavia; in Britain it is mainly confined to southern England and is very rare. In southern Europe there are several other species of *Gryllotalpa* that are very similar in appearance but often live in drier places.

Oecanthus pellucens ♀, Oberbergen KS, August
Gryllotalpa gryllotalpa ♂, (Mkt. Rettenbach Ag), May

FAMILY TETRIGIDAE (ground-hoppers)

The ground-hoppers have the striking feature of a pronotum extending backwards into a pointed spike, which reaches at least to the tip of the abdomen, often well beyond it. The hind-margin of each pronotal side-flap has two bulges (only one in nymphs), above which lies the fore wing, reduced to a small scale. The hind wings, however, can be fully developed. Stridulatory and hearing organs are absent. Ground-hoppers overwinter as either nymphs or adults. Reliable identification of the European species is very difficult.

Tetrix subulata (Slender Ground-hopper)
(= *Acrydium subulatum*)
The keel along the back of the pronotum is almost straight in side view. The tip usually extends well beyond the tip of the abdomen; under the pronotum lie the fully-developed hind wings, reaching to its tip. The species flies readily and is difficult to catch. However, in addition to the form with fully-developed pronotum, there is also a shortened, flightless form, usually in smaller numbers. In contrast to the following species, the distance between the eyes, seen from above, is greater than their diameter (particularly noticeable in the female). The colour varies greatly: reddish, yellow-brown and black, and very variably marked insects occur together. The body-length (measured without the pronotal extension) varies between 7 and 12mm. The females are (as in all ground-hoppers) distinguished by the ovipositor, which in side view is two-valved (actually four-valved) and toothed above and below. Adults occur from August; they live until June/July of the following year.

The Slender Ground-hopper is almost confined to damp places, especially dried-out waterside mud-flats. It also sometimes occurs in sand-pits. It is found throughout Europe and occurs locally in southern Britain and Ireland.

The food consists of grasses, mosses and lichens. In the silent courtship display the male bows in front of the female and vibrates his wings. As in other ground-hoppers the eggs are laid in groups above or below the surface of the earth.

Tetrix subulata ♀, Langenau SA, September
 Tetrix subulata ♀, shortened form, Langenau SA, September

FAMILY TETRIGIDAE (ground-hoppers)

Tetrix ceperoi (Cepero's Ground-hopper)

Cepero's Ground-hopper is very difficult to distinguish from the Slender Ground-hopper. It is somewhat smaller and more delicate (7–10mm without the pronotal extension). In side view, the keel along the back of the pronotum is slightly more strongly arched behind the head than in *T. subulata*. The vertex, measured between the eyes, is hardly wider than an eye and projects forwards only slightly. The adult life-span is comparable to that of the Slender Ground-hopper.

Tetrix ceperoi is widespread in southern Europe, and occurs only patchily further north. In Britain it occurs locally in southern England and south Wales, mainly near the coast. It lives in damp sand-pits and mud-flats, often together with *T. subulata*.

Tetrix tuerki (Türk's Ground-hopper)

Tetrix tuerki is the third species of *Tetrix* with an almost straight keel along the back of the pronotum. However, the species usually has a short pronotum and a distinctly broader build than both the foregoing species. A further striking character is provided by the clearly undulating underside of the mid femora. The colouring is usually uniformly grey or brown; however, mottled insects occur. The body-length reaches 7–10mm. It is also mainly adults that overwinter in this species (they can be found throughout the year).

Tetrix tuerki has very narrow ecological requirements. It lives only on the silty gravel-banks of streams, particularly in the Alps, but also in uplands further east in Europe. Absent from Britain.

Tetrix ceperoi ♀, (Pula Is), September
Tetrix tuerki ♀, (Huben Ty), August

FAMILY TETRIGIDAE (ground-hoppers)

Tetrix undulata (Common Ground-hopper)

(= *T. vittata*)

The keel along the back of the Common Ground-hopper is clearly arched in side view. This insect is a little more slender than both the following species. The hind femora are about three times longer than deep. The hind wings are at least twice as long as the scale-like fore wings (rarely longer). The pronotum reaches about as far as the hind knees. The colouring varies greatly, but yellow-brown to grey-brown insects, with darker mottling, predominate. The body-length reaches 8–11mm. The species overwinters as nymphs or adults, and adults can be found throughout the year.

Tetrix undulata occurs in moderately damp places. It lives most frequently in forest glades, but also in meadows and moorland that is not too damp. It is widely distributed in central, western and northern Europe, reaching northern Spain in the south. It is widespread in the British Isles, where it is the commonest species of *Tetrix* (as elsewhere in the northern part of its range).

Tetrix tenuicornis (Long-horned Ground-hopper)

(= *T. nutans*)

Tetrix tenuicornis is distinctly more thick-set than *T. undulata*. The hind femora are less than three times as long as deep. The antennae are noticeably long and slender, the middle segments about four times as long as wide. The hind wings are less reduced than in *T. undulata*; they reach almost to the tip of the pronotum. The colouring is also very variable in this species: blackish-brown or grey with varied markings. There are often two black spots on the pronotum, as in the following species. The body-length reaches 8–10mm. The species overwinters mostly as nymphs, but one can find adults throughout the year.

Tetrix tenuicornis occurs predominantly in dry places. It is found most frequently in sand-pits, quarries and dry grassland with sparse vegetation. It is very widespread in Europe, but becomes scarcer in the west, where the climate is more oceanic. Absent from Britain.

Tetrix undulata ♂, (Ulm SA), September
Tetrix tenuicornis ♀, (Lautern SA), September

FAMILY TETRIGIDAE (ground-hoppers)

Tetrix bipunctata (Two-spotted Ground-hopper)

(= *Acrydium bipunctatum*)

The Two-spotted Ground-hopper is very similar to the foregoing species, *T. tenuicornis*. It has, however, distinctly shorter and thicker antennae (the middle segments are only about twice as long as wide). There is a further difference in the pronotum: viewed from above its front margin clearly projects forwards into an angle (rounded in *T. tenuicornis*). Two forms can be distinguished by the length of the hind wings: in f. *kraussi* they are about double, in f. *brachyptera* about three times the length of the fore wings. Since the two forms also differ ecologically (see below), one could well regard them as subspecies. Some authors even consider them to be species (Fischer 1948). Both forms very rarely occur with extended pronotum and fully developed hind wings. The colour and pattern are again extremely variable. There is, however, almost always a pair of blacker or greyer spots on the pronotum; hence the name of the species. One often finds very contrastingly pale and dark mottled insects. The species is 8–11mm in size and overwinters as adults. Adult insects occur throughout the year.

Tetrix bipunctata is more restricted to dry habitats than any of the other ground-hoppers. The form *brachyptera* occurs predominantly in dry alpine meadows, f. *kraussi* in other habitats, such as dry calcareous grassland. The species is widespread in northern and central Europe, from Scandinavia to the Pyrenees and Alps, but does not occur in Britain.

Tetrix bipunctata f. *kraussi* ♀, Suppingen SA, September
Tetrix bipunctata f. *brachyptera* ♀, Längenfeld Ty, August

FAMILY CATANTOPIDAE (spine-breasted grasshoppers)

The spine-breasted grasshoppers are distinguished from the other grasshoppers (family Acrididae) by the cylindrical spine between the coxae of the fore legs. This is clearly visible to the naked eye (one must of course hold the insect in the hand). The tympanal organs form oval or semicircular openings on the sides of the first abdominal segment. There are no stridulatory organs, but the insects produce a sound by grinding the mandibles against each other – 'gnashing their teeth', so to speak. The family is distributed mainly in warmer regions; in north-west Europe there are only three species.

Podisma pedestris (Brown Mountain Grasshopper)
Podisma pedestris is red-brown in ground colour, variegated with yellow and black markings. The hind femora are pale red on the underside and the hind tibiae blue. The fore wings are reduced to small lobes shorter than the pronotum. However, specimens with fully-developed flight organs occasionally occur. The males are 17–19mm, the females 24–30mm long. The species is sometimes already adult in June and lives until October.

The Brown Mountain Grasshopper lives in dry woodland glades overgrown with heather, in dry alpine meadows (up to 2600m) and occasionally on moors. It occurs mainly on mountains and is widespread in Europe from Scandinavia to the Alps and across the Pyrenees to central Spain. Absent from Britain.

Both sexes can produce soft crackling sounds with the mandibles, e.g., when handled. During courtship the male slowly stalks the female, making rocking movements with his body.

Podisma pedestris ♂, (Obergurgl Ty), July
Podisma pedestris ♀, (Obergurgl Ty), July

FAMILY CATANTOPIDAE (spine-breasted grasshoppers)

Miramella alpina (Green Mountain Grasshopper)

(= *Podisma alpina*)

Miramella alpina is bright green. On each side of the pronotum there is a black longitudinal stripe, which (particularly in the male) has a downward extension. The hind femora are red below; the hind tibiae are yellowish in the female, very dark blue in the male, pink towards the tip. The whole body has erect pale hairs. The pale brown fore wings are about as long as the pronotum or longer (up to more than half the length of the abdomen). The species is very variable in colour, markings and length of fore wings. The males are distinctly more colourful than the females. The body-length varies between 16 and 23mm (♂) or 22 and 31mm (♀). The insects are sometimes already adult in June, but more usually in the middle of July, and live until September.

Miramella alpina is a mountain grasshopper, usually occurring between 1000 and 2800m. It is widespread in the mountains of western and central Europe, but does not reach as far north as Scandinavia or further south than the southern foothills of the Pyrenees and Alps; it is absent from Britain. In contrast to *Podisma pedestris*, the Green Mountain Grasshopper prefers damp places, especially lush meadows and the vegetation around springs with stands of butterbur; large numbers are often found on the butterbur itself, the leaves of which are frequently eaten away. Sometimes both mountain species occur together, especially at very high altitudes.

Both sexes, and also the nymphs, make sounds with their mandibles. After mating, the male often allows himself to be carried about by the female for some time.

Miramella alpina ♂, (Oberstdorf Ag), July
Miramella alpina ♀, (Oberstdorf Ag), July

FAMILY CATANTOPIDAE (spine-breasted grasshoppers)

Calliptamus italicus (Italian Locust)

The Italian Locust is grey-brown to red-brown in colour. A yellowish longitudinal stripe often runs along each side of the pronotum and fore wings. The fore wings are in addition dark-spotted; they reach to about the hind knees. The hind wings are tinted in the basal half with a beautiful rose-red; elsewhere they are transparent. The hind tibiae are bright red. The male has a conspicuous copulatory apparatus with long and robust, curved cerci. The body-length varies between 15 and 23mm (♂) or 23 and 34mm (♀); the larger measurements apply to southern insects. It is adult in July/August and lives until October.

The Italian Locust is very dependent on warm and dry conditions. It lives only in very dry places with sparse vegetation, such as dry rocky grassland and sandy steppe. It is very common and widespread in southern Europe, becoming scarcer further north and seldom occurring north of 50°N latitude; it is absent from Britain. There are several other very similar species of *Calliptamus* in southern Europe, but none of these occurs as far north as the Italian Locust.

Calliptamus italicus is very lively in warm conditions and flies readily in spite of its stout build. Although the Italian Locust is well camouflaged when sitting still, the red hind wings and hind tibiae make it very conspicuous in flight. The males stridulate freely with their mandibles when they meet others of their kind. The sounds are audible from about 50cm and are accompanied by vigorous twitching movements of the antennae, palps and hind femora. For mating, the male approaches the female in jerks, but cautiously, making gradually quieter mandible-sounds. Eventually he grasps the tip of the female's abdomen with a sudden movement, and mating follows.

Calliptamus italicus ♂, Premantura Is, September

 Calliptamus italicus, ♀ in flight, (Rothenbrunnen Gr), August

FAMILY ACRIDIDAE (grasshoppers)

The Acrididae are the largest family of Orthoptera. They lack the spine between the fore coxae that is typical of the spine-breasted grasshoppers. In some species, however, there is a smaller, conical protuberance. Most of the European species stridulate by rubbing the hind femora against the fore wings. The hearing organs lie on each side of the first abdominal segment.

Subfamily Locustinae

The Locustinae are usually round-headed in side view. Their hind wings are often brightly coloured. They rub a smooth stridulatory keel on the inner side of the hind femur against a raised, toothed stridulatory vein in the medial area of the fore wing. Well-defined courtship songs are absent.

Psophus stridulus (Rattle Grasshopper)

The Rattle Grasshopper has a continuous, prominent keel along the top of the pronotum, with small grooves running sideways from it. The females are usually yellow-brown or grey, the males almost black. The wings are shortened in the large, heavy females, but the males are fully winged. In both sexes the wings are bright red with blackish-brown tips. The females are 26–40mm long, the males only 23–25mm. Adult insects found from July/August to October.

This species lives in dry, usually stony places, in warm, dry fields, and also in mountains up to about 2000m. It has a wide distribution in Europe, from parts of Scandinavia to northern Spain, northern Italy and Yugoslavia. Absent from Britain.

Males fly with a loud rattling sound, which is produced by the hind wings. Together with the strikingly bright red wings, this may serve to startle potential enemies. It also has a function in courtship. In cooler weather and after repeated disturbance, the insects fly quietly. The females can rattle while sitting or jumping.

Psophus stridulus, ♂ in flight, (Lautern SA), August
Psophus stridulus ♀, Lautern SA, August

FAMILY ACRIDIDAE (grasshoppers)

Subfamily Locustinae

Locusta migratoria (Migratory Locust)
(= *L. danica*, *Pachytylus migratorius*)
With a body-length of 32–54mm, *Locusta migratoria* is one of the largest European Orthoptera. It occurs in two, clearly distinguished forms, which were once regarded as separate species. Normally it develops as the solitary phase (phasis solitaria = *Locusta danica*). In this phase there is a prominent keel, with an indentation in the middle, along the pronotum. The fore wings are less than double the length of the hind femora. The ground colour is mostly green; the hind tibiae are red. In the migratory phase (phasis gregaria), on the other hand, there is a less prominent keel, depressed in the middle, and the fore wings are usually more than double the length of the hind femora. The ground colour is brown with two black longitudinal stripes on the pronotum, and pale yellow hind tibiae. There are transitional forms between the two phases. Adults occur from June to October; in the Mediterranean they overwinter and can be found in April.

In Europe, the Migratory Locust is primarily a Mediterranean insect. The solitary phase occurs regularly in this region. Under very favourable conditions, the insects breed extremely prolifically, developing, under the influence of 'population pressure', into the migratory phase. In this phase the locusts are much livelier than in the solitary phase, forming swarms and invading new territory. The eggs laid in the 'foreign country' develop normally – i.e., without too high a population pressure – into solitary locusts; these may form a population lasting several years, or die out in an unfavourable year. In this way, locusts have occurred repeatedly in northern Europe in the past – sometimes as destructive swarms and sometimes as inconspicuous, sedentary populations; a few migrants even reach Britain from time to time.

Locusta migratoria breeds predominantly in damp, sandy places. The swarms usually come from the extensive fertile plains of the lower Danube. As these breeding grounds have now been largely destroyed by cultivation, swarms are no longer likely to threaten northern Europe.

Locusta migratoria ♀, solitary phase, Talamone Tu, April
Locusta migratoria ♀, migratory phase (insect from a culture), December

FAMILY ACRIDIDAE (grasshoppers)

Subfamily Locustinae

Oedipoda caerulescens (Blue-winged Grasshopper)
The Blue-winged Grasshopper is extremely variable in colour: red-brown, grey, yellowish, even almost black or almost white – depending on the background on which it has developed. The fore wings are marked with two or three dark transverse bands. The hind wings are bright pale blue with a blackish-brown, curved cross-band and a transparent apical part. The top of the hind femur bears one or two dark spots and is clearly stepped near the middle. The hind tibiae are grey-blue, ringed with black and white at the base. The keel on the top of the pronotum is indented just in front of the middle. The body-length reaches 15–21mm (♂) or 22–28mm (♀). One finds adults from July to October.

This species has a strong preference for dry places. It lives, for example, in dry, stony fields with sparse vegetation, in quarries and sand-pits. It occurs very abundantly in many localities, especially in warm regions. It is very widespread in Europe, from southern Sweden in the north to the whole of the Mediterranean region. Absent from Britain.

Oedipoda caerulescens usually adapts its colour to its background: insects on limestone, for instance, are generally pale grey but on clay soil are yellow-brown. The colour adaptation is achieved by the formation of matching pigments during nymphal development. The flash of the blue hind wings is always quite startling when this camouflaged grasshopper takes off – and when it lands it suddenly disappears. Sound-production is of no great importance in this species. The male produces quite short, soft sounds immediately before mating. Food consists mostly of grasses.

Oedipoda caerulescens ♂, Heroldingen NöR, September
 Oedipoda caerulescens, ♀ in flight, (Jockgrim Pf), September

FAMILY ACRIDIDAE (grasshoppers)

Subfamily Locustinae

Oedipoda germanica (Red-winged Grasshopper)

The Red-winged Grasshopper closely resembles its blue-winged sister species. The colour also varies from pale grey to dark brown or blackish according to the colour of the background. A clear distinction is provided by the red hind wings, which can be, in rare cases, yellowish. The blackish-brown band on the hind wing is generally more extensive than in *Oe. caerulescens*. It runs along almost the whole of the hind margin, bending towards the front shortly before the wing-tip and finally running parallel to the fore-margin in a long-drawn-out point. Sometimes the band reaches the wing-tip, so that the transparent part of the wing is absent. A further distinguishing character lies in the step on the top of the hind femur: it is less sharply defined in *Oe. germanica* than in *Oe. caerulescens*. A final character, not easy to see, lies on the forehead between the antennae. In this region the blue-winged species has a median longitudinal keel, which is absent in the red-winged species. The adults occur at the same time (July to October) in both species.

Oedipoda germanica also likes warm and dry places, but is distinctly more particular than *Oe. caerulescens*. It lives only in barren, stony or rocky places, often on steep southern slopes and frequently in the vicinity of vineyards. It is largely absent from sandy soils. It often occurs together with the Blue-winged Grasshopper and sometimes the Italian Locust. It is less widespread than the Blue-winged Grasshopper, not reaching northern Germany and, although occurring in most of southern Europe, is confined to Catalonia in Spain. Absent from Britain.

The Red-winged Grasshopper hardly differs in behaviour from the blue-winged species. The males often chase the females of the other species, but cross-mating apparently does not occur. When photographing these insects it is essential to note the wing-colour, as it is very difficult to identify the species solely from a photograph of a sitting insect.

Oedipoda germanica ♂, Schlossböckelheim Pf, August
Oedipoda germanica, ♀ in flight, (Chur Gr), August

FAMILY ACRIDIDAE (grasshoppers)

Subfamily Locustinae

Bryodema tuberculata (Speckled Grasshopper)

The Speckled Grasshopper is one of the largest and most attractive grasshoppers in Europe. The males reach 26–31mm, the females 29–39mm in body-length. Like most Locustinae this species is very inconspicuous when sitting still. The colouring is grey, brown, even blackish or slightly greenish. The fore wings are usually clearly speckled, sometimes with a suggestion of transverse bands. The hind wings are very broad, almost butterfly-like, especially in the male. They are rose-coloured in the basal part, elsewhere brown, and rather transparent towards the tip, where they are brown-speckled. Alternate longitudinal veins are thickened and strongly rose-coloured. The pronotum is rugose with a granular surface, its weak median keel interrupted by two transverse grooves. The hind tibiae are yellow. Adults occur from July or August to September.

The Speckled Grasshopper occurs in two quite different habitats: sandy heaths with sparse vegetation in the north, and almost barren gravel-banks of alpine rivers and streams in the south. It is primarily an eastern European species, but it occurs very patchily in central and even northern Europe (including parts of Scandinavia and Germany) and the Alps. It is not known from west of Germany and Switzerland, or from anywhere in southern Europe.

Bryodema tuberculata is a very good flier. Disturbed males fly effortlessly for 50m, producing, at the same time, a melodious whirring sound, much softer than in *Psophus stridulus*. The females also fly with a whirring sound, but only for short distances. The insects can also fly silently. During courtship the whirring male flies round the stationary female.

Bryodema tuberculata, ♂ in flight, (Lechtal Ty), September

Bryodema tuberculata ♀, Lechtal Ty, August

FAMILY ACRIDIDAE (grasshoppers)

Subfamily Locustinae

Sphingonotus caerulans (Slender Blue-winged Grasshopper)

The Slender Blue-winged Grasshopper resembles the *Oedipoda* species, but lacks the step on the top of the hind femur typical of that genus. It is also slimmer and has longer wings. When the hind legs are fully extended backwards, the wing-tips reach to about the ends of the hind tibiae (in *Oedipoda* to no further than the middle). The hind wings are blue at the base, transparent in the apical part. There is sometimes a suggestion of a dark band in the northern subspecies (*S. caerulans cyanopterus*). The colouring is as variable as in *Oedipoda*. The fore wings are marked with two or three dark transverse bands or with uniform fine speckles ('sand-coloured'). The median keel of the pronotum is indistinct towards the front and interrupted by three transverse grooves. The head projects well above the pronotum in side view. The hind tibiae are pale blue. The body-length reaches 14–26mm (♂) or 20–31mm (♀). Adults occur from August to October.

Sphingonotus caerulans lives typically in barren areas of dry sand and gravel. The species often occurs in association with *Oedipoda caerulescens*, but probably never with *Oedipoda germanica*. Except for the extreme north, it is found throughout continental Europe, including southern Scandinavia and Finland, and also occurs on many of the Mediterranean islands. Absent from Britain.

The Slender Blue-winged Grasshopper is an outstanding flier. The males are visually attracted to flying females. When several males are together they produce short, trilling sounds.

Sphingonotus caerulans ♂,
Jockgrim Pf, August
Sphingonotus caerulans ♀,
in flight, (Jockgrim Pf), September

FAMILY ACRIDIDAE (grasshoppers)
Subfamily Locustinae

Aiolopus thalassinus (Long-winged Grasshopper)
(= *Epacromia thalassina*)
Like the following three species, the Long-winged Grasshopper is reminiscent of the Gomphocerinae in general appearance, but is placed in the Locustinae because of the structure of the stridulatory apparatus. It reaches 15–19mm (♂) or 21–25mm (♀) in body-length. The ground colour is green or (less often) brown, with very distinctive markings. The fore wings usually have two pale transverse bands and large dark spots. The hind wings are often tinted with very pale green at the base and grey-brown at the tip. The hind tibiae are ringed with black and white at the base; elsewhere they are red or yellow. Adults occur August–October.

This species lives in damp places, especially on the banks of small stretches of still water, and sometimes also in sand-pits. It occurs throughout southern and (patchily) central Europe, including much of central and southern France and southern Germany. Absent from Britain. There is a very similar species, *Aiolopus strepens*, that is also widespread in southern Europe, but does not occur quite as far north (absent from Germany and not reaching central France). It may be distinguished from *A. thalassinus* by its deeper hind femora (less than three and a half times as long as deep, compared with at least four times in *A. thalassinus*.

Epacromius tergestinus (Eastern Long-winged Grasshopper)
(= *Aiolopus tergestinus*)
The Eastern Long-winged Grasshopper closely resembles *Aiolopus thalassinus* and is comparable in size and time of appearance. The ground colour is usually brown or reddish, rarely green. The fore wings are quite finely spotted, without clear bands. The hind tibiae are bluish. *Epacromius tergestinus* lives predominantly on muddy gravel-banks of alpine streams. It is primarily an eastern European and Asian species, but occurs locally in central and southern Europe, including France, northern Spain and Italy, not Britain.

Aiolopus thalassinus ♀, Jockgrim Pf, August
Epacromius tergestinus ♀, specimen from Augsburg, leg. Fischer, August 1939

FAMILY ACRIDIDAE (grasshoppers)

Subfamily Locustinae

Stethophyma grossum (Large Marsh Grasshopper)

(= *Mecostethus grossus*)

The Large Marsh Grasshopper is olive green to brown in ground colour. The females sometimes have patches of purple-red. The fore wings have a yellow stripe along the anterior (= lower) margin. The hind femora are red (rarely yellow) below, the hind tibiae yellow with black rings and spines. The pronotum has almost straight side-keels in addition to a median keel. There is a small conical protuberance between the fore coxae. The size varies greatly, from 12 to 25mm (♂) or 26 to 39mm (♀). Adults can be found between July and October.

The Large Marsh Grasshopper lives only in damp places. It inhabits wet meadows, water margins, even quaking bogs on moors. However, it does not occur on the *Sphagnum* moss of high moors. It occurs widely in Europe north of the Pyrenees and Alps, reaching as far north as Lapland, but it is found only in the extreme north of the southern peninsulas. In the British Isles it is extremely local in southern England and western Ireland.

Both sexes of *Stethophyma grossum* are good fliers. The males produce snapping sounds audible from about 10m. To do this they lift one hind leg (sometimes both) and flick the tibia backwards. In this way the apical spines of the hind tibia are struck against the fore wing. These tibial 'flick-sounds' are produced in an irregular series as the calling song, and also by both sexes, when disturbed, as a defensive sound. The egg-pods are laid densely in the vegetation, above or below the surface of the soil.

Stethophyma grossum ♂, Rotenburg LH, July
Stethophyma grossum ♀, Arnegg SA, September

FAMILY ACRIDIDAE (grasshoppers)

Subfamily Locustinae

Mecostethus alliaceus (Leek Grasshopper)

(= *Parapleurus alliaceus*)

The Leek Grasshopper is usually pale yellow-green, occasionally olive green or brown. A sharply-defined black stripe runs from each eye along the side of the pronotum to about the middle of the fore wing. Below this stripe the fore wings are pale green. The body-length varies from 17 to 23mm (♂) or 28 to 32mm (♀). The adults appear in August and live until October.

The Leek Grasshopper lives mainly in damp meadows and around water, but also occurs in dry meadows with long grass. This species is found mainly in the southern part of central Europe, including south and south-west Germany, France, Switzerland and Austria; it occurs only in the extreme north of the southern peninsulas. Absent from Britain.

Subfamily Gomphocerinae*

Arcyptera microptera (Small Banded Grasshopper)

(= *Stethophyma flavicosta*)

The Small Banded Grasshopper reaches 19–22mm (♂) or 24–29mm (♀) in body-length. The colouring is olive green to brown. The fore wings have a whitish stripe along the fore margin; the hind wings are transparent. The pronotum has angled side-keels. There is a small conical protuberance between the fore coxae. The species is one of the earliest Orthoptera; it is sometimes already adult at the end of May and lives until September.

Arcyptera microptera is a typical steppe-dweller. It occurs very locally in south-east France, the northern half of Spain, Switzerland, Austria and further east. Absent from Britain.

* Description of the subfamily on the following page.

Mecostethus alliaceus ♀, Eriskirch OS, August
Arcyptera microptera ♂,
specimen from Vienna, leg. Fruhstorfer 1920

FAMILY ACRIDIDAE (grasshoppers)

Subfamily Gomphocerinae

The Gomphocerinae include a host of grasshopper species living in countless meadows and other kinds of grassland. They usually have pointed heads in side view. The stridulatory apparatus consists of a smooth vein on the fore wing and a keel with fine pegs on the inner side of the hind femur. The songs are very varied and characteristic. In most species there are different types of song, the principal ones being the calling song (to attract the female), rivalry song (when males meet) and courtship song (in pairing). In the song descriptions I have usually restricted myself to the calling songs, as these are most often heard. It is sometimes very difficult to identify the species, but studying the songs makes it much easier even in the difficult cases.

Arcyptera fusca (Large Banded Grasshopper)

(= *Stethophyma fusca*)

In its colouring and size (23–36mm in the male, 29–40mm in the female), the Large Banded Grasshopper is one of the most impressive of the western European grasshoppers. The ground colour is yellowish to olive, with yellow and black markings. The bright red hind tibiae have a black and a yellow ring at the base. The fore wings are yellow-striped and blackish-brown in the apical part, like the hind wings. In the females the wings are shortened. The side-keels of the pronotum are almost straight. The adults live from July to September.

This beautiful grasshopper occurs mainly on mountains, from the Pyrenees, Jura and Alps (including south-west Germany) to the mountains of eastern Europe; it is absent from Britain. It lives in dry alpine meadows with poor vegetation, and on heaths.

The males, which are very proficient fliers, produce a rattling sound in flight, which is softer than in *Psophus* and *Bryodema*. On landing they often produce a loud, rasping 're' by a single, short stroke of the hind femora against the fore wings. The same sound is produced together with a whirring sound in the calling song, roughly 're-chshsh-re-re'.

Arcyptera fusca ♂, Augsburg, September
Arcyptera fusca ♀, Augsburg, September

FAMILY ACRIDIDAE (grasshoppers)

Subfamily Gomphocerinae

Chrysochraon dispar (Large Gold Grasshopper)

The two sexes of the Large Gold Grasshopper are very different from each other. The female is 22–30mm in size and is brown in colour, with a slight metallic lustre. The hind tibiae and the undersides of the hind femora are wine-red. The greatly shortened, lobe-like fore wings almost touch each other in the middle of the back. The males are only 16–19mm in size and are shiny pale green with a metallic lustre. The fore wings are clearly longer; they reach almost to the tip of the abdomen. The hind wings are reduced to very small vestiges. The hind tibiae and the undersides of the hind femora are yellow, the hind knees dark. Fully-winged individuals (*p. 38*, below) occasionally occur in both sexes. Adults are already about at the end of June and live until September, sometimes October.

Chrysochraon dispar usually lives in damp places, especially damp meadows and the edges of ditches. Sometimes, however, it occurs in dry areas with long grass and woodland borders. It is distributed widely in northern and central Europe, from Finland to the southern slopes of the Pyrenees and Alps, including France and Germany. Absent from Britain.

The song consists of short chirps *c.* 0.5–1 sec. long, which follow one another at intervals of about 5–10 sec. A single chirp is composed of three to nine syllables and can be represented as ‘zizizizizi’. Egg-laying takes place only in plant-stems, never in the ground. For this purpose the female usually chooses dead woody shoots that have broken off such plants as raspberry and golden-rod. She pushes the tip of the abdomen through the broken end into the pith-filled cavity by pushing the pith aside with the valves of the ovipositor (*p. 19*, above). In this way she penetrates about 4cm deep into the interior of the stem, extending the abdomen telescopically. The eggs deposited there are embedded in a quick-setting foamy secretion (*p. 24*, above right). Ramme (1927) gives a detailed description of egg-laying in this species.

Chrysochraon dispar ♂, Baustetten OS, August
Chrysochraon dispar ♀, Baustetten OS, August

FAMILY ACRIDIDAE (grasshoppers)

Subfamily Gomphocerinae

Chrysochraon brachypterus (Small Gold Grasshopper)
(= *Euthystira brachyptera*)
The Small Gold Grasshopper resembles its larger sister species, especially in the male. The body-length varies between 13 and 17mm (♂) or 18 and 26mm (♀). Both sexes are usually pale green with a metallic lustre. The very small, scale-like fore wings of the female are pink or (less often) yellow-green; they are separated from each other on the back by a wide gap. The valves of the ovipositor are greatly lengthened, almost like those of a bush-cricket. The fore wings of the male almost reach the middle of the abdomen and are truncate (and usually somewhat emarginate) at the tip. The hind knees are not darkened. The species is sometimes already adult at the beginning of June and lives until September.

Chrysochraon brachypterus is equally at home in damp and dry habitats. It lives in marshy meadows as well as dry fields with long grass, sometimes even extremely dry, stony places. It occurs from central Germany in the north to the Pyrenees and Alps in the south, including uplands in France and the whole of central Europe. Absent from Britain.

The song is very soft, audible from about 3m and consisting of quite short chirps with four to six syllables, which merge at higher temperatures into a short 'zrrr'. Egg-laying in this species also takes place above ground. The female folds leaves (usually of grasses) with her hind legs, and lays eggs in the fold – often also between two leaves – and embeds them in a quick-setting foamy liquid. The egg-pods, which later become brown, contain five to six eggs (*p. 24*, below right).

'sochraon brachypterus ♂, Suppingen SA, September
'ysochraon brachypterus ♀, Baustetten OS, August

FAMILY ACRIDIDAE (grasshoppers)

Subfamily Gomphocerinae

Stenobothrus lineatus (Stripe-winged Grasshopper)

In the genus *Stenobothrus* (in contrast to *Chorthippus*) there is no bulge on the anterior margin of the fore wing (the lower margin of the flexed wing); its medial area is often broadened, with regular cross-veins (in contrast to *Omocestus*). In the females, the ovipositor valves are toothed. In the north-west European species the side-keels of the pronotum are incurved, about one and a half times further apart at the back than at the narrowest point.

With a body-length of 15–19mm (♂) or 21–26mm (♀), the Stripe-winged Grasshopper is the largest northern European species in the genus. The ground colour is usually green, less often brown or red-violet. The insects are often very variegated. In the male the tip of the abdomen is mostly red. The wings are fully developed in the male, very slightly shortened in the female. There is an oblique white mark at the end of the broad medial area; in the female there is, in addition, a whitish longitudinal stripe along the anterior margin of the fore wing. Adults occur from the beginning of July until October.

Stenobothrus lineatus prefers dry places. It is one of the dominant grasshoppers of heathland and dry grassland, and can also be found on roadsides and wasteland, more rarely in fairly damp meadows. Widespread in Europe from southern Sweden to the southern peninsulas, where it is confined to mountains. In Britain it occurs locally in southern England.

The calling song is one of the most characteristic grasshopper songs. It consists of a buzzing sound lasting 10–20 sec., regularly rising and falling in pitch (comparable to a siren). It is rather soft and hesitant at the start, but soon reaches full intensity (when it is audible from about 5m). The start can be represented as 'zi-zi-zuizuizuizui . . .'. During the song one hind femur is drawn across the fore wings slightly in advance of the other, so that they are temporarily displaced (see upper illustration). The courtship song in front of the female is quite different: in its first phase consisting of short, sharp sounds ('tsitsitsitsi'); in its second, like the calling song. The egg-pods are laid above the roots of grasses.

Stenobothrus lineatus, ♂ singing, Riedheim BS, August
Stenobothrus lineatus ♀, Lautern SA, September

FAMILY ACRIDIDAE (grasshoppers)

Subfamily Gomphocerinae

Stenobothrus nigromaculatus (Black-spotted Grasshopper)

The Black-spotted Grasshopper is only a little smaller than the similar species *S. lineatus*: 13–18mm (♂) or 18–25mm (♀). The ground colour is green or pale brown, the tip of the male's abdomen mostly red. The wings are distinctly shortened in the female, and much narrower than the hind femora; they end well short of the tip of the abdomen. In the male, they are only slightly shortened, and just about reach the tip of the abdomen. The medial area is much narrower than in *S. lineatus* and clearly more than half the length of the fore wing; in this area there is a row of square spots, which stand out more clearly in the female than in the male. Adults occur from July to October.

Stenobothrus nigromaculatus lives in very dry places with sparse vegetation, occurring, for example, on dry stony grassland, steppe-like gravelly plains and sand-dunes. It occurs almost as widely in Europe as *S. lineatus*, but is much more local; it does not reach as far as northern France and northern Germany, and in Spain is found only around the Pyrenees. Absent from Britain.

The calling song consists of a series of (usually three) whizzing sounds. Each of these begins softly, rapidly increasing to full intensity and ending abruptly after about 1 sec. Between these sounds there are slightly longer pauses. Two males often respond to each other, one always singing in the pauses in the other's song. The variable courtship song also includes quite different buzzing and ticking sounds.

Stenobothrus nigromaculatus ♂, Winden Bu, July

 Stenobothrus nigromaculatus ♀, Heroldingen NöR, September

FAMILY ACRIDIDAE (grasshoppers)
Subfamily Gomphocerinae

Stenobothrus stigmaticus (Lesser Mottled Grasshopper)

The Lesser Mottled Grasshopper looks like a small edition of *S. lineatus*. It is only 11–15mm (♂) or 15–20mm (♀) in size. The ground colour is almost always green, the tip of the male abdomen red. The female's fore wings are shortened and rather narrower than the hind femora. This reduction in length is especially noticeable in older females, when the stretched abdomen is full of eggs (the lower illustration shows a young female). In the male the wings are fully developed; the medial area is only slightly broadened. In this respect it is very similar to *Omocestus* spp. While the female is clearly recognizable as *Stenobothrus* from the toothed ovipositor valves, recognition of the male, in particular distinguishing it from *Omocestus haemorrhoidalis*, sometimes causes difficulties. Two further characters help here: there is a yellow-brown longitudinal stripe, narrowly bordered with black, on each side of the top of the head behind the eyes, interrupting the green ground colour; in addition, the side-keels of the pronotum are much less strongly incurved. Adults occur from June/July to October.

The Lesser Mottled Grasshopper lives only in warm, dry places, with very short grass, and is a typical inhabitant of sheep pasture. It is very frequently found in association with *S. lineatus* and *O. haemorrhoidalis*. It occurs widely in western and central Europe (including France and Germany), but not as far north as Scandinavia; in the south it occurs in the mountainous parts of the Iberian Peninsula and in Yugoslavia, but in Italy it is confined to the Italian Alps. In the British Isles it is known only from the Isle of Man.

The song is very soft and consists of a sequence of similar, rapidly repeated syllables, sounding like 'chichichichi . . .'. A sequence lasts no more than 3 sec.; the next one follows after a longer interval. The song of *Stenobothrus stigmaticus* is also reminiscent of *Omocestus haemorrhoidalis*.

Stenobothrus stigmaticus ♂, Rammingen SA, August
Stenobothrus stigmaticus ♀, Rammingen SA, August

FAMILY ACRIDIDAE (grasshoppers)

Subfamily Gomphocerinae

Omocestus viridulus (Common Green Grasshopper)

In the genus *Omocestus* – as in *Stenobothrus* – there is no bulge on the anterior margin of the fore wing (in contrast to *Chorthippus*); the medial area is not broadened (in contrast to *Stenobothrus*). The side-keels of the pronotum are angularly bent; they are twice as far apart at the back as at the angle. The ovipositor is not toothed.

The Common Green Grasshopper is extremely variable in colouring: green, brown, red or yellowish, often very colourfully marked. The insect is frequently brown or red on the sides and bright green above. The tip of the abdomen is never red. The fore wings are not or hardly spotted, but often green above. The body-length varies between 13 and 17mm (♂) or 20 and 24mm (♀). The females can closely resemble those of *Stenobothrus lineatus* or *Omocestus rufipes*. The species is adult very early, from the middle of June, and lives until August/September, exceptionally October.

The Common Green Grasshopper is a typical inhabitant of moderately damp to dry mountain meadows, where it is one of the dominant Orthoptera. It is also common, however, in the lowlands of northern and western Europe, and its range extends northwards over most of Scandinavia. It becomes less common in the southern peninsulas, where it is usually confined to mountains. Common throughout the British Isles.

The song is easy to recognize. It consists of a conspicuous ticking sound, increasing in loudness and lasting for about 10–20 sec. It is strikingly reminiscent of a rapidly rattling alarm clock.

Omocestus viridulus ♂, Gerhausen SA, July
Omocestus viridulus ♀, Langenau SA, September

FAMILY ACRIDIDAE (grasshoppers)

Subfamily Gomphocerinae

Omocestus rufipes (Woodland Grasshopper)

(= *O. ventralis*)

The Woodland Grasshopper is one of the most attractive Orthoptera. The female closely resembles that of *O. viridulus*. The most striking character is the underside of the abdomen: it is greenish at the front, yellow in the middle and bright red towards the tip – as in a rainbow. The black, white-tipped palps provide an additional colour character.

The same colour pattern is shown by the male (*p. 11*, below left). There is a further difference in the fore wings, in which the medial area is usually spotted in *O. rufipes* but only sometimes and rather weakly so in *O. viridulus*. The hind wings are clearly darkened in the apical half. While the females are mostly blackish-brown on the sides and bright green above, the males are dark brown to black, often yellow-brown above and always with the tip of the abdomen blood-red. In the male the hind tibiae, and often the femora, are red. The body-size reaches 12–17mm (♂) or 18–21mm (♀). Adults are found from the beginning of July until November.

Omocestus rufipes usually lives in dry, sometimes extremely dry places, perhaps together with *Psophus stridulus* and *Platycleis albopunctata* in rocky, almost barren grassland, with *Myrmeleotettix maculatus* on dry paths on moors, or with both the other *Omocestus* spp. on close-cropped sheep pasture. Its distribution in Europe is very similar to that of *O. viridulus*, but it is less common in the north and occurs more widely in the southern peninsulas. Local in southern England and south Wales.

The song sounds very similar to that of *O. viridulus*. It is distinctly shorter, however, lasting about 5 sec.

Omocestus rufipes ♂, Lautern SA, September
Omocestus rufipes ♀, Lautern SA, September

FAMILY ACRIDIDAE (grasshoppers)

Subfamily Gomphocerinae

Omocestus haemorrhoidalis (Orange-tipped Grasshopper)

With a body-length of 10–14mm (♂) or 16–19mm (♀), the Orange-tipped Grasshopper is the smallest *Omocestus* sp. in northern Europe. The ground colour is paler or darker brown, sometimes green above, especially in the male. The tip of the abdomen is reddish-yellow, but never such a fiery red as in *O. rufipes*. The palps are uniformly pale grey. The fore wings are clearly spotted in the medial area, the hind wings transparent, almost glass-like, and slightly darkened only at the tip. The species is very inconspicuous and easily confused with other grasshoppers, the female particularly with *Myrmeleotettix maculatus*, the male with *Stenobothrus stigmaticus*. Adult insects occur from the beginning of July until October.

Omocestus haemorrhoidalis likes warm, dry conditions. It occurs mainly on dry pastureland and in sandy areas. It is widely distributed in Europe, from the Baltic island of Gotland to uplands in the southern peninsulas. Absent from Britain.

The song is very soft and consists of a rapid succession of similar syllables, which sound like 'shishishishi . . .' and are grouped together into chirps lasting for about 3 sec. At higher temperatures the syllables follow one another so rapidly that they merge together into a uniform chirp. The chirps follow one another at rather irregular intervals.

Omocestus haemorrhoidalis ♂, Riedheim BS, September
Omocestus haemorrhoidalis ♀, Rammingen SA, September

FAMILY ACRIDIDAE (grasshoppers)
Subfamily Gomphocerinae

Gomphocerus sibiricus (Club-legged Grasshopper)
(= *Aeropus sibiricus*)
The antennae of the Club-legged Grasshopper are broadened at the tip and thus club-shaped. This broadening is visible only from above or below, however, as the tips of the antennae are flattened in side view. The ground colour is brown, green or yellowish, often with different colours combined. The fore wings have a bulge on the anterior margin and are slightly shortened in the female. The medial area is broadened (as in *Stenobothrus*). The male is unmistakable, with its swollen, bladder-like fore tibiae (*p. 11*, below right). The pronotum, moreover, is humpbacked, often strongly so, in side view (much less so in the female). The body-length varies between 18 and 23mm (♂) or 19 and 25mm (♀). Adults occur from July to September.

The Club-legged Grasshopper occurs widely in the mountains of central and southern Europe, including the Pyrenees and Alps, and some of the mountains of the southern peninsulas; it is absent from Britain. It begins to be found at about 1000m, but occurs commonly only at heights of around 2000m. It lives in dry alpine meadows with sparse vegetation, especially on south-facing, grassy slopes, but also in alpine rose scrub. Occurs up to 2600m (in Switzerland).

The loud song of *Gomphocerus sibiricus* in a calm high alpine valley is a memorable sound. Two types of song are usually dominant. One is the rivalry song, a harsh 'trrrt', reminiscent of the sound made by *Chorthippus brunneus*, and often produced in a rather similar way by two males alternating. The other type of song, the calling song, consists of rapidly repeated, very loud syllables (*c.* 5 per sec.), which sound like 'tre' and are produced in a sequence lasting about 15–20 sec. Several males often sing exactly synchronously, but regularly-alternating songs also occur. During courtship in front of the female, still further different sounds are produced, and also almost pantomime-like movements: the bladder-like fore tibiae of the male are important in giving optical signals; their function is otherwise unknown.

Gomphocerus sibiricus ♂, Hochgurgl Ty, July
Gomphocerus sibiricus ♀, Hochgurgl Ty, July

FAMILY ACRIDIDAE (grasshoppers)

Subfamily Gomphocerinae

Gomphocerippus rufus (Rufous Grasshopper)

(= *Gomphocerus rufus*)

The tips of the antennae of the Rufous Grasshopper are markedly broadened (especially in the male). These antennal clubs are black with white tips. The ground colour varies between red-brown and grey-brown; yellowish tints also occur. The fore wings have a bulge on the anterior margin; the medial area is not broadened. The body-length reaches 14–16mm (♂) or 17–24mm (♀). The first adults are found in July, but nymphs still occur in September. The insects survive until October/November.

The Rufous Grasshopper lives in fairly damp to fairly dry places, especially along sunny forest borders and in forest clearings, but also in dry grassland. It stays on the ground less than other grasshoppers; it likes to sun itself, for example, on bramble bushes. It occurs from the southern half of Scandinavia and Finland in the north to mountains in Italy and Yugoslavia in the south, but is absent from the Iberian Peninsula; it occurs up to about 2000m in the Alps. Very local on limestone vegetation in southern England and South Wales.

The song consists of a sequence of rapidly repeated, sibilant syllables, which sound rather like 'sh-sh-sh-sh . . .'. The sequence lasts on average for 5 sec. and contains about thirty such syllables together. During courtship in front of the female a three-phased courtship song is produced, accompanied by expressive movements of the antennae and palps. The female lays her egg-pod in the ground. She closes the hole resulting from egg-laying by means of scraping and stamping movements of the hind legs.

Gomphocerippus rufus ♂, Arnegg SA, August
Gomphocerippus rufus ♀, Auendorf SA, September

FAMILY ACRIDIDAE (grasshoppers)

Subfamily Gomphocerinae

Myrmeleotettix maculatus (Mottled Grasshopper)

(= *Gomphocerus maculatus*)

The male of the Mottled Grasshopper has well-developed, uniformly dark-coloured antennal clubs, which are usually bent outwards. In the female, on the other hand, the broadening of the antennae is hardly noticeable. The ground colour is usually red-brown to yellow-brown, often also green or colourfully mottled. In the male the abdominal tip is usually red. The insects are often remarkably well adapted to the background, especially the females. There is no bulge on the anterior margin of the fore wing; the medial area is slightly broadened and dark-spotted. With a body-length of only 11–13mm (♂) or 12–17mm (♀), this species is one of the smallest grasshoppers in northern Europe. The female in particular is easy to confuse with that of *Omocestus haemorrhoidalis*. It is, however, somewhat more thickset (for example, the pronotum, viewed from above, is only about as long as the head, distinctly longer in *O. haemorrhoidalis*). The adult life-span is very long, extending from the middle of June to October.

The Mottled Grasshopper lives exclusively in dry places with sparse vegetation. It is often very common on heathland and sand-dunes, as well as the driest parts of moors, but is only rarely found on dry, calcareous grassland. It occurs very widely in Europe, from the southern half of Scandinavia and Finland to mountains in the southern peninsulas. Widespread in Britain and Ireland.

The song is soft, but highly characteristic. It consists of a sequence, *c.* 10 sec. long, of buzzing sounds, each of which lasts barely 0.5 sec., and separated by short pauses, roughly 'rrr-rrr-rrr-rrr . . .'. The last few sounds are rather more widely-spaced.

Myrmeleotettix maculatus ♂, Gosheim NöR, August
Myrmeleotettix maculatus ♀, Betzhorn LH, August

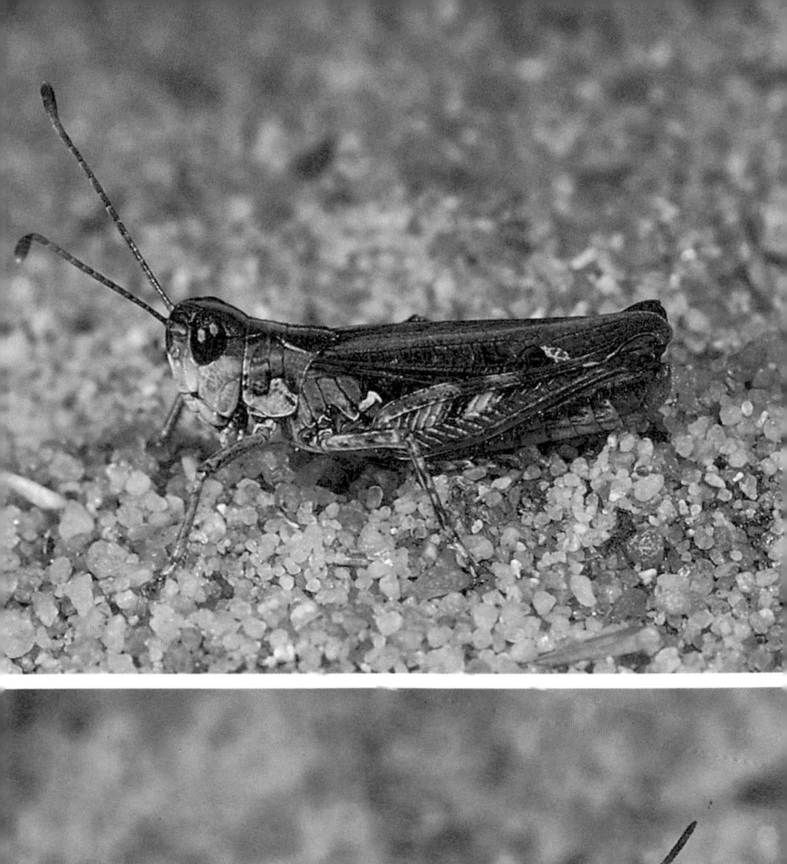

FAMILY ACRIDIDAE (grasshoppers)
Subfamily Gomphocerinae

Stauroderus scalaris (Large Mountain Grasshopper)
(= *S. morio, Chorthippus scalaris*)

The Large Mountain Grasshopper is closely related to *Chorthippus* and is now frequently included in that genus (Harz 1975). In the male the medial and costal areas of the fore wing are conspicuously widened with very regular cross-veins. In the female the medial area is also widened, but has a network of veinlets. The hind wings of both sexes, and also the tips of the male fore legs, are dark brown. The ground colour is otherwise brown, yellowish or olive green. The hind tibiae are red or yellow. With a body length of 18–21mm (♂) or 23–27mm (♀), the Large Mountain Grasshopper is rather larger than the northern European *Chorthippus* species. It is adult from July to September.

Stauroderus scalaris prefers to live in dry, stony mountain meadows. It occurs widely in the mountains of central and southern Europe, from Germany southwards through France and the whole of the Alps (up to about 2000m), to the northern and central parts of the southern peninsulas. Absent from Britain.

The Large Mountain Grasshopper produces a very rich repertoire of sounds; I restrict myself here to the most important ones. The calling song is composed of two different elements, a soft buzzing sound produced by rapid up-and-down movements of the femora ('dsh') and a harder rattling sound produced by a single high stroke of the femora ('trr'). These sounds alternate in sequences of varying duration: 'dsh-trr-dsh-trr-dsh-trr . . .'. There is always a soft sound at the beginning and a hard sound at the end. In addition, both sexes produce a soft rattling sound in flight, much softer than in *Psophus stridulus*.

Stauroderus scalaris ♂, (Huben Ty), August
Stauroderus scalaris ♀, Reichenay Gr, July

FAMILY ACRIDIDAE (grasshoppers)

Subfamily Gomphocerinae

Chorthippus apricarius (Upland Field Grasshopper)

Species with very different characters are grouped together in the genus *Chorthippus*. All of them (except the male of *Ch. albomarginatus*) have in common a distinct bulge on the anterior margin of the fore wing. The ovipositor valves are, in addition, untoothed. There is much variation in the wing-venation and the shape of the pronotal side-keels.

The Upland Field Grasshopper belongs to the subgenus *Glyptobothrus*, which is distinguished from *Chorthippus* s. str. by its angularly-bent pronotal side-keels. Like *Stauroderus scalaris*, *Chorthippus apricarius* has broadened costal and medial areas, which have regular cross-veins in the male. In the female, both these wing-areas have a network of veinlets. The hind wings are transparent. The ground colour is generally pale yellow-brown, less often red-brown, with only weakly-developed darker markings. The tympanal opening is oval. The body-length reaches 13–16mm (♂) or 16–22mm (♀). Adults occur from July to October.

Chorthippus apricarius prefers poor, dry, sandy soil, but also occurs on dry, calcareous grassland. It lives especially on dry, grassy waysides among cornfields or meadows. It occurs from southern Sweden to the Pyrenees, Alps and Apennines, and in southern and western Europe is generally found only in hills and mountains. Absent from Britain.

The pale colouring of the Upland Field Grasshopper makes it a very inconspicuous species. It often reveals itself, however, by its characteristic song. The syllables are composed of two different sound elements, one percussive ('k') and one frictional ('chi'). The percussive element is usually produced only in every second syllable. The syllables are arranged successively in long sequences, sounding rather like 'kchichi-kchichi-kchichi . . .'. The sequences begin softly, soon reach full intensity and end suddenly. The song sounds rather like hissing and puffing; hence the species has been called '*Locomotiefje*' in Holland.

Chorthippus apricarius ♂, Zurndorf Bu, July
Chorthippus apricarius ♀, Zurndorf Bu, July

FAMILY ACRIDIDAE (grasshoppers)

Subfamily Gomphocerinae

Chorthippus pullus (Gravel Grasshopper)

(= *Glyptobothrus pullus*, *Stauroderus pullus*)

The Gravel Grasshopper's wings are shortened in both sexes; in the male they reach to about the tip of the abdomen, in the female to the middle. Fully-winged individuals are very rare. The ground colour, including the fore wings, is mostly red-brown or grey-brown, less often yellowish. There are two dark spots on the top of the hind femora; the hind knees are black. There is a marked contrast between the inconspicuous ground colour and the bright blood-red hind tibiae. The tympanal opening is oval. The body-size varies between 12 and 17mm (♂) or 18 and 22mm (♀). Adults occur from July to October.

Chorthippus pullus is very like the Speckled Grasshopper in its requirements, living on the gravel-banks of alpine streams and on sandy heathland. It is a mainly central and eastern European species, but occurs very locally in southern Germany, the French Alps, Switzerland, Austria and the Italian Alps. Absent from Britain.

The song is a continuous chirp lasting 1–2 sec. and sounding rather like 'zzzzz'. It resembles the song of *Stenobothrus nigromaculatus*, but is softer and more uniform. *C. pullus* does not produce a sequence of several chirps, as is typical of *S. nigromaculatus*, and there is no special courtship song.

Chorthippus pullus ♂, (Huben Ty), August
Chorthippus pullus ♀, Obersdorf Ag, September

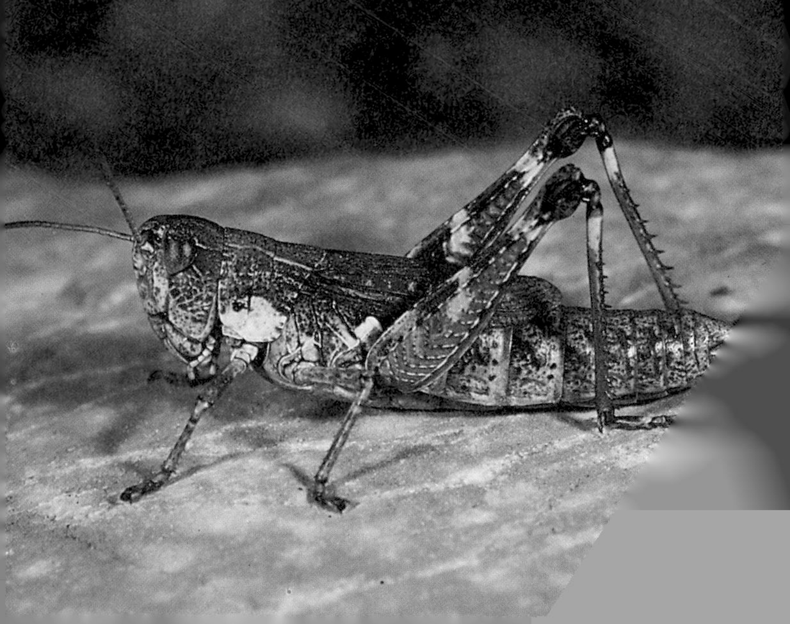

FAMILY ACRIDIDAE (grasshoppers)

Subfamily Gomphocerinae

Chorthippus vagans (Heath Grasshopper)

(= *Glyptobothrus vagans*, *Stauroderus vagans*)

The Heath Grasshopper is very similar to the *biguttulus*-group that follows. It can be distinguished from them most reliably by the oval tympanal opening and the song (see below). The ground colour is dark brown to yellowish; the tip of the abdomen is red in both sexes. Above the sides of the pronotum are two broad, black, longitudinal stripes, through which run the sharply-defined, white, angled side-keels. The hind tibiae are red or yellow. The fore wings usually reach only to the hind knees. In general appearance and the shape of the fore wings (as well as in habitat) this species most resembles *Ch. mollis*, but is generally darker and more variegated. The body-length varies between 12 and 15mm (♂) or 16 and 22mm (♀). Adults are found from July/August to October.

Chorthippus vagans lives in warm, dry places with sparse vegetation. It occurs particularly on rocky heathland, but also on sand-dunes and in open pine-woods. It occurs widely in central and southern Europe, from as far north as Denmark to the whole of the Iberian Peninsula, much of Italy and Yugoslavia. In Britain it is confined to sandy heaths in south-east Dorset and the extreme west of Hampshire.

The song is rather characterless. It consists of a long, regular sequence of similar scraping sounds, about five per sec., roughly 'tretretre . . .'. The rivalry song is formed by breaking up the same sounds into irregular shorter series, e.g., 'tretre-tre-tretretre-tretre- . . .'.

Chorthippus vagans ♂, Eichstätt FrA, August
Chorthippus vagans ♀, Eichstätt FrA, August

FAMILY ACRIDIDAE (grasshoppers)

Subfamily Gomphocerinae

Chorthippus biguttulus (Bow-winged Grasshopper)
(= *Glyptobothrus biguttulus*, *Stauroderus biguttulus*, *Stauroderus variabilis* part.)
The Bow-winged Grasshopper belongs to a group of species with narrow, kidney-shaped tympanal openings (*biguttulus*-group) that are difficult to identify. The three representatives in northern Europe were once considered to belong to a single species (*Stauroderus variabilis*) that was very variable in the shape of the fore wings. Although it had long been evident that some insects had narrow, long fore wings and others short, broad fore wings, 'intermediate forms' appeared so frequently that it seemed impossible to separate clearly even two species. It was not until Ramme studied the songs that it was shown that three different species were confused under the collective name *St. variabilis* (Ramme 1921). In *Chorthippus biguttulus* the fore wings are comparatively short and broad. In the male the costal area is broadened; the costa joins the subcosta at an angle near the wing-tip. The breadth of the fore wing is 3mm in both sexes, the length 12mm in the male, 15mm in the female (mean values). This gives a length:breadth ratio of 4 (♂) or 5 (♀). The colouring shows no reliable characteristics: it varies enormously, especially in the female, and can be, for example, red-brown, blackish-brown, grey, green or rose-red (see lower illustration). The abdominal tip is red in the male, but not in the female. The size varies between 13 and 15mm (♂) or 17 and 22mm (♀). Adults occur from the middle of July until November. The Bow-winged Grasshopper is one of the most common Orthoptera in northern and central Europe, occurring from Scandinavia and Finland to the Pyrenees and Alps. It lives in fairly dry places, such as meadows or waysides, and is abundant throughout its range. It does not, however, occur in the British Isles. The song consists of loud ringing chirps, which are among the typical summer sounds f a continental meadow. They begin with clearly-separated okes, which follow one another ever more closely, at the e time becoming louder, and end after 2–3 sec: 'tttttrrrrt'.

Chorthippus biguttulus ♂, Langenau SA, September
Chorthippus biguttulus ♀, red colour variety, Hirschau near Tübingen, September

FAMILY ACRIDIDAE (grasshoppers)

Subfamily Gomphocerinae

Chorthippus brunneus (Field Grasshopper)

(= *Glyptobothrus brunneus*, *Stauroderus brunneus*, *S. bicolor*, *S. variabilis* part.)

The Field Grasshopper is on average a little larger than *Ch. biguttulus*. It reaches 14–18mm (♂) or 19–25mm (♀) in body-length. Its fore wings are longer and relatively narrower. In the male the costal area is hardly widened; the costa joins the subcosta without an angle. The fore wings average 3mm in breadth and reach a length of 14.5mm in the male, 18mm in the female. This gives a length:breadth ratio of 4.8 (♂) or 6 (♀). The ratio can be easily measured if the grasshopper is photographed exactly from the side. The colouring is as variable as in the foregoing species. The abdominal tip is red above in the male and often also in the female. Adult insects occur from the beginning of July until October.

Chorthippus brunneus is rather more dependent on dry habitats than *Ch. biguttulus*. It lives, for example, in sand-pits, on dry grassland and in dry forest clearings. Although very widespread, it is less common than the Bow-winged Grasshopper in continental Europe. It occurs from Scandinavia and Finland to the Pyrenees and Italy; it is widespread in the British Isles (including Scotland and Ireland), and is particularly common in the southern half of Britain.

The song is very striking and easily remembered. It consists of hard 'sst'-sounds of about 0.2 sec. duration. These are produced in a monotonous series at 2 sec. intervals. As soon as one male hears the song of another he joins in. There is then a very regular 'alternation song' between the two insects, in which one sings exactly in the pauses in the other's song, roughly:

'sst – sst – sst',
'sst – sst – sst – .

The upper line represents one male, the lower one the other. One can also stimulate the insects to sing by imitating their song oneself, and actually take part in an 'alternation song' with a grasshopper!

Chorthippus brunneus ♂, Ringingen SA, September
Chorthippus brunneus ♀, Ringingen SA, September

FAMILY ACRIDIDAE (grasshoppers)

Subfamily Gomphocerinae

Chorthippus mollis (Lesser Field Grasshopper)

(= *Glyptobothrus mollis*, *Stauroderus mollis*, *S. variabilis* part.)

The Lesser Field Grasshopper is the third northern European species in the *biguttulus*-group. The validity of the species was clearly established only through the study of the song. It is somewhat smaller than both the other species, 12.5–14mm (♂) and 17–19mm (♀). (These measurements apply only to central European insects.) In wing characteristics the species is intermediate between *Ch. biguttulus* and *Ch. brunneus*. In the male, the costal area is widened rather more than in *Ch. brunneus* and rather less than in *Ch. biguttulus*; the costa joins the subcosta at a very slight angle. The fore wings are only 2.5mm wide, 12mm long in the male, 15mm long in the female. The length:breadth ratio is 4.8 (♂), 6 (♀) – the same values as in *Ch. brunneus*. Most insects are an inconspicuous grey-brown; the tip of the male abdomen is only rarely reddish. Adults occur from July to October.

Chorthippus mollis is more particular in its requirements than the other species of the *biguttulus*-group. It is almost confined to hot, dry places, such as dry, rocky grassland and heath. It generally occurs in association with *Ch. biguttulus* and *Ch. brunneus*, and often also *Ch. vagans*. It is found from southern Sweden to the Pyrenees and Alps, but is absent from Britain. The song provides the easiest and most reliable way of recognizing *Ch. mollis*. It is noteworthy that the two hind femora produce different sounds that merge into one. One femur produces a percussive sound ('ts'), the other a whirring sound ('rrr'); the two components form a 'tsrrr'. In the course of a sequence lasting about 20 sec., there are about fifty to sixty of these sounds, changing in the relative share of the percussive and whirring components: at first only percussive sounds are heard, then the whirring sounds are added, softly at first but becoming increasingly loud, until at the conclusion the percussive strokes are completely suppressed. In an abbreviated form such a sequence sounds like: 'ts-ts-tsr-tsr-srr-tsrr-tsrrr-tsrrr-rrrr-rrrr'. The sequence ends with a few, ore spaced-out 'rrr'-sounds.

Chorthippus mollis , ♂ singing, Lautern SA, September

Chorthippus mollis ♀, Lautern SA, August

FAMILY ACRIDIDAE (grasshoppers)

Subfamily Gomphocerinae

Chorthippus dorsatus (Steppe Grasshopper)

The Steppe Grasshopper and the remaining *Chorthippus* species belong to the subgenus *Chorthippus* s. str. The members of this subgenus have pronotal side-keels that are straight or slightly incurved but never angularly bent. They tend to live in damp places, whereas the species of the foregoing subgenus occur predominantly in dry places.

In *Chorthippus dorsatus* the pronotal side-keels are nearly parallel (or very slightly converging) in the anterior third, clearly diverging in the posterior two-thirds. The colouring is usually uniformly brown or olive green, often grass-green on top and brown elsewhere. Markings are largely absent (very rarely there is a white wing-stripe in the female). There is often a slight metallic lustre. The tip of the male abdomen is red. The body-length is 14–18mm (♂) or 19–25mm (♀). Adults occur from July to September.

Chorthippus dorsatus prefers to live in moderately damp meadows, especially on the edges of moors, but also in drier places. It occurs widely in Europe, from southern Sweden and Denmark to northern Spain, Italy and Yugoslavia. Absent from Britain.

The song consists of short, scraping chirps as in *Chorthippus parallelus*. At the end of each chirp, however, there is always a sizzling sound. Such a chirp sounds like 'rererereredsh' and lasts about 1 sec.

Chorthippus dorsatus ♂, Baustetten OS, September
Chorthippus dorsatus ♀, Baustetten OS, September

FAMILY ACRIDIDAE (grasshoppers)
Subfamily Gomphocerinae

Chorthippus albomarginatus (Lesser Marsh Grasshopper)

(= *Ch. elegans*)

The Lesser Marsh Grasshopper resembles the Steppe Grasshopper, especially the male. In both sexes, however, the pronotal side-keels are almost completely straight, diverging slightly from front to back. The colouring is brown, grey, yellowish or green. The female is often green on top and otherwise brown. The anterior margin of the fore wing has a slight bulge in the female but not in the male (an exception in the genus *Chorthippus*). In the female, there is almost always a white longitudinal stripe along the costal area; this is usually absent in the male. The sigmoid curve of the radius is a distinguishing feature in the male fore wing. The body-length varies between 13 and 15mm (♂) or 18 and 21mm (♀). Adults occur from July to October.

The Lesser Marsh Grasshopper lives in fairly damp or marshy meadows, and also salt-marshes near the coast. It occurs very widely in Europe, from the southern half of Scandinavia and Finland to Spain, Italy and Yugoslavia. It is local in the southern half of Britain, especially near the coast, and has been recorded from Co. Clare in Ireland.

The song resembles those of *Stenobothrus nigromaculatus* and *Chorthippus brunneus*. It usually consists of three uniformly loud chirps (not increasing in intensity as in *S. nigromaculatus*) lasting about 0.5 sec. (thus longer than in *Ch. brunneus*). These chirps sound rather like 'rrrrt'. There is often also an 'alternation song' between two males.

Chorthippus albomarginatus ♂, (Ulm SA), September
Chorthippus albomarginatus ♀, Rammingen SA, August

FAMILY ACRIDIDAE (grasshoppers)
Subfamily Gomphocerinae

Chorthippus parallelus (Meadow Grasshopper)
(= *Ch. longicornis* part.)
The wings are shortened in both sexes of the Meadow Grasshopper. The fore wings reach to near the tip of the abdomen in the male, to about its middle in the female. In the male fore wing the stigma (a region of thickened veinlets that shows up as a whitish or brownish spot) is no more than 1.5mm from the wing-tip. If a male is held against the light, it can be seen that the short hind wings end well before the stigma. In the female, the reduced fore wings are pointed at the tip. Occasionally fully-winged individuals occur. The ovipositor valves are clearly shorter than in the following species. The ground colour varies between green, brown, yellowish and reddish; colourfully mottled insects also occur. The pronotal side-keels are parallel or slightly converging in the anterior third, diverging in the posterior two-thirds. The hind knees are dark. The body-length reaches 13–16mm (♂) or 17–23mm (♀). Adult insects appear from June/July, and can still be found in November.

The Meadow Grasshopper is probably the commonest species of Orthoptera in northern Europe. It is most abundant in fairly damp meadows, but also occurs on dry grassland, waysides and moors. It is usually absent from extremely dry and very wet places. Together with *Metrioptera roeselii*, it is one of the last species to survive in richly fertile meadows. It has a very wide European distribution, extending northwards into the lower parts of Scandinavia and even beyond the Arctic Circle in Finland. In the southern peninsulas it occurs mainly in mountains. It is widespread and common in Britain (where it sometimes occurs in wetter conditions than on the Continent), but absent from Ireland and the Isle of Man.

The song consists of short chirps composed of rapidly repeated scraping sounds. Such a chirp sounds like 'zrezrezrezrezre' and lasts at least 1 sec. The chirps follow one another at intervals of about 3 sec.

Chorthippus parallelus ♂, Riedheim BS, July
Chorthippus parallelus ♀, Riedheim BS, July

FAMILY ACRIDIDAE (grasshoppers)
Subfamily Gomphocerinae

Chorthippus montanus (Water-meadow Grasshopper)
(= *Ch. longicornis* part.)
Chorthippus montanus resembles the foregoing species so closely that the two were put together for a long time under the name *Ch. longicornis*. There were repeated attempts to separate them (beginning 150 years ago), but these were always rejected by later authors. It was only through a thorough study of the song that a clear separation became possible (Faber 1929). Distinguishing between the two species by morphological characteristics is often difficult. In the male Water-meadow Grasshopper, the stigma is at least 2.5mm from the tip of the fore wing, and the hind wings reach almost, or completely, to it. In the female, the tips of the fore wings are more broadly rounded; the ovipositor valves are clearly longer in the other species. In other characteristics, as well as in size, the two species are largely similar. Fully-winged individuals also sometimes occur, and in the female there is every intermediate form between short-winged and fully-winged. Adults occur from July to October.

The Water-meadow Grasshopper is distinctly less common than *Ch. parallelus*. It lives mainly in marshy meadows and quaking bogs, often in association with *Stethophyma grossum* and the *Conocephalus* species. Occasionally, however, it is found in rather drier places, where it can occur in a mixed population with the Meadow Grasshopper. It is almost as widespread in Europe as *Ch. parallelus*, but much more local. Absent from Britain.

The song is louder but somewhat less harsh than in *Ch. parallelus* and, above all, distinctly slower. The chirps also consist of uniform syllables, which sound like 'shr-shr-shr . . .'. A single chirp lasts about 2–3 sec.; the next follows after an interval of about 5 sec.

Chorthippus montanus ♂, Baustetten OS, August
Chorthippus montanus ♀, Arnegg SA, September

List of technical terms, abbreviations and symbols

♂ male
♀ female
abdomen (*adj.* **abdominal**) the third and last division of the body
anal vein(s) the most posterior longitudinal wing-vein(s)
c. about
cercus (*pl.* **cerci**) one of the paired pincer- or spike-like abdominal appendages
clypeus a shield-like plate on the lower front of the head
compound eye one of the paired main eyes, composed of numerous 'simple eyes'
costa the first (most anterior) longitudinal wing-vein
costal area the wing area just behind the costa
coxa (*pl.* **coxae**) the first division of the leg
cubital area the wing area just behind the costa
cubitus the fifth longitudinal wing-vein (usually divided into two)
femur (*pl.* **femora**) the third division of the leg
foveola (*pl.* **foveolae**) one of the paired depressions on each side of the vertex in grasshoppers
habitus body-build, general appearance
hygrophilous moisture-loving
I-00 figures illustrating the identification key
instar the stage between two successive moults, or following the final moult
intercalary vein an extra longitudinal wing-vein inserted between two of the main veins
labium the lower lip, behind the maxillae
labrum the upper lip, in front of the mandibles
larva (*pl.* **larvae**) the young stage (between egg and pupa) of insects that undergo complete metamorphosis
leg. collected
mandible one of the paired jaws
maxilla (*pl.* **maxillae**) one of the paired mouthparts behind the mandibles
media the fourth longitudinal wing-vein
medial area the wing area just behind the media
mesonotum the plate covering the top of the middle segment of the thorax
mesopleuron the plate on the side of the middle segment of the thorax
mesosternum the plate underneath the middle segment of the thorax
metamorphosis the change in body-form during development from larva to adult
metanotum the plate covering the top of the last segment of the thorax
metapleuron the plate on the side of the last segment of the thorax
metasternum the plate underneath the last segment of the thorax
metazona the part of the top of the pronotum behind the transverse groove
nymph the young stage between the egg and the adult
ocellus (*pl.* **ocelli**) one of the three small simple eyes
Orthoptera the bush-crickets, crickets, ground-hoppers and grasshoppers, together with the cockroaches, praying mantises and earwigs
ovipositor the structure at the tip of the female abdomen used for egg-laying
palps the two pairs of small, segmented appendages of the maxillae and labium
precostal area the wing area in front of the costa
pronotal side-flaps the vertical sides of the pronotum

pronotal side-keels the slightly-raised ridges sometimes present on each side of the top of the pronotum
pronotum the large, saddle-shaped plate covering the first segment of the thorax
prosternum the plate underneath the first segment of the thorax
prozona the part of the top of the pronotum in front of the transverse groove
radius the third longitudinal wing-vein
S–00 song-diagrams
spermatophore the container in which the sperms are transferred from the male to the female
sternite the plate underneath one segment of the body
stigma a small region of thickened veinlets on the fore wings of some grasshoppers, often showing up as a pale-coloured spot
stridulation sound- production by rubbing one structure against another
style one of the small paired appendages on the male subgenital plate of some bush-crickets
subcosta the second longitudinal wing-vein
subgenital plate the last abdominal sternite
substrate the material on which an animal moves or rests
syllable the sound produced by one complete to-and-fro movement of the fore wings (crickets and bush-crickets) or up-and-down movement of the legs (grasshoppers)
tarsus (*pl.* **tarsi**) the foot; the segmented last division of the leg
tergite the plate covering the top of one segment of the body
thorax the middle division of the body
tibia (*pl.* **tibiae**) the fourth division of the leg
trochanter the small, second division of the leg
tympanum (*adj.* **tympanal**) the thin membrane of the hearing organ
valve one of the paired components of the ovipositor
vertex the front part of the top of the head

Abbreviations of regional names used in the legends to the photographs:

Ag	Allgäu (West Germany)
BaW	Bayerischer Wald (West Germany)
Bd	Baden (West Germany)
BS	Bayerisches Schwaben (West Germany)
Bu	Burgenland (Austria)
FrA	Fränkische Alb (West Germany)
Gr	Graubünden (Switzerland)
Is	Istria (Yugoslavia)
LH	Lüneburger Heide (West Germany)
NöR	Nördlinger Ries (West Germany)
OS	Oberschwaben (West Germany)
Pf	Pfalz (West Germany)
SA	Schwäbische Alb (West Germany)
Sl	Slovenia (Yugoslavia)
Tu	Tuscany (Italy)
Ty	Tyrol (Austria)
( )	photograph not taken at the original locality

Bibliography

BELLMANN, H. (1985). *Die Stimmen der heimischen Heuschrecken.* Tape cassette. Neumann-Neudamm, Melsungen.

BROWN, V.K. (1983). *Grasshoppers.* Cambridge University Press. 65pp.

FABER, A. (1929). Die Lautäusserungen der Orthopteren I. *Z. Morph. ökol. Tiere* **13**, 745–803.

FABER, A. (1953). *Laut- und Gebärdensprache bei Insekten. Orthoptera (Geradflügler) I.* Staatliches Museum für Naturkunde in Stuttgart. 198pp.

FISCHER, H. (1948). Die schwäbischen *Tetrix*-Arten. *Ber. naturf. Ges. Augsburg* **1**, 40–87.

GREIN, G. (1984). *Gesänge der heimischen Heuschrecken. Akustische-optische Bestimmungshilfe.* 30cm disc. Niedersächsisches Landesverwaltungsamt, Hannover.

HAES, E.C.M. (1979). *Provisional atlas of the insects of the British Isles. Part 6. Orthoptera* (second edition). Biological Records Centre, Huntingdon. 40pp.

HARZ, K. (1969). Die Orthopteren Europas I. *Series ent.* **5**, 749pp.

HARZ, K. (1975). Die Orthopteren Europas II. *Series ent.* **11**, 939pp.

HÖLLDOBLER, K. (1947). Studien über die Ameisengrille (*Myrmecophila acervorum* Panzer) in mittleren Maingebiet. *Mitt. schweiz. ent. Ges.* **20**, 607–648.
HOLST, K.T. (1986). The Saltatoria (bush-crickets, crickets and grasshoppers) of Northern Europe. *Fauna ent. scand.* **16**, 127pp.
INGRISCH, S. (1977). Beitrag zur Kenntnis der Larvenstadien mitteleuropäischer Laubheuschrecken (Orthoptera: Tettigoniidae). *Z. angew. Zool.* **64**, 459–501.
INGRISCH, S. (1982). Orthopterengesellschaften in Hessen. *Hess. faun. Briefe* **2**, 38–46.
MARSHALL, J.A. (1974). The British Orthoptera since 1800 (pp. 307–322). In HAWKSWORTH, D.L. (Ed.), *The changing flora and fauna of Britain.* Academic Press, London & New York. xiv + 462pp.
OSCHMANN, M. (1969). Bestimmungstabellen für die Larven mitteldeutscher Orthopteren. *Dt. ent. Z.* (N.F.) **16**, 277–291.
RAGGE, D.R. (1965). *Grasshoppers, crickets and cockroaches of the British Isles.* Warne, London. xii + 299pp.
RAGGE, D.R. (1973). The British Orthoptera: a supplement. *Entomologist's Gaz.* **24**, 227–245.
RAMME, W. (1921). Orthopterologische Beiträge. *Arch. Naturgesch.* (A) **86** (1920), 81–166.
RAMME, W. (1927). Die Eiablage von *Chrysochraon dispar* Germ. (Orth. Acrid.). *Z. Morph. ökol. Tiere* **7**, 127–133.

Index